SNOTGIRL: CALIFORNIA SCREAMING

Script: BRYAN LEE O'MALLEY
Art: LESLIE HUNG
Colors: RACHAEL COHEN
Lettering: MARÉ ODOMO

Created by
BRYAN LEE O'MALLEY & LESLIE HUNG

Originally serialized as SNOTGIRL #6-10.
Special thanks to STUDIO JFISH

Standard ISBN: 978-1-5343-0661-5
Barnes & Noble Exclusive ISBN: 978-1-5343-0914-2

SNOTGIRL, VOL. 2: CALIFORNIA SCREAMING. First printing. May 2018. Contains material originally published in single magazine form as SNOTGIRL #6-10. Published by Image Comics, Inc. Office of publication: 2701 NW Vaughn St., Suite 780, Portland, OR 97210.

06. SINCE YOU'VE BEEN GONE
WE'RE ALL CONNECTED. I MEAN IN A COSMIC SENSE.
A BUTTERFLY FLAPS ITS WINGS, AND... YOU KNOW. SCIENCE.
OR ANYWAY THAT'S HOW IT USED TO BE. THESE DAYS I'M NOT SO SURE.
THESE DAYS...
...THINGS SEEM TO HAPPEN FOR NO REASON AT ALL.
SO YEAH, I KNOW, IT LOOKS BAD, BUT THIS TIME...
...I SWEAR IT WASN'T MY FAULT!

Morning.

UGHHHH...

EVERYTHING.

I KNOW THIS IS A CONTROVERSIAL TOPIC, BUT GUYS....
WE NEED TO OPEN UP.
Sunday, 10:22 AM
WE NEED A NEW MEMBER! THREE PEOPLE ISN'T ENOUGH. WHAT IF WE WANT TO SHARE WAFFLES?
PLUS IT'S AWKWARD WHEN ONE OF US SKIPS! BRUNCH FOR TWO IS *SAD!*
YOU'RE THE ONLY ONE WHO EVER WANTS WAFFLES, MEG! WE *HATE* WAFFLES.
WELL, I LIKE WAFFLES, BUT I HATE NEW PEOPLE!
YOU CAN'T *HATE* NEW PEOPLE, SILLY. YOU HAVEN'T EVEN MET THEM YET!
IMAGINE IF THAT HAD BEEN MY ATTITUDE THE NIGHT I MET ASHLEY! DO YOU THINK THIS RING WOULD BE ON MY FINGER?
WHAT IS THIS NONSENSE? WE'RE LITERALLY AT *HATERS' BRUNCH*!
I'LL HATE WHOEVER AND WHATEVER I PLEASE!
WE'RE HATERS! WE HATE!
I WANTED TO CALL IT *BLOGGERS'* BRUNCH.
OF COURSE YOU DID, MEG...

CLATTER
YOU!
YES, IT'S ME! BONNIE...
...YOUR IDENTICAL TWIN SISTER!
HER WHAT?!
BONNIE SUTTON
identical twin

IT'S WILD RUNNING INTO YOU, SIS!
I'M HERE WITH MY FAMILY-- YOU SHOULD JOIN US.
A HUSBAND AND KID?!
SCREAMING
IS THIS REAL? IS THIS REALLY HAPPENING??
OKAY... WHO GAVE YOU THE LOCATION OF THIS BRUNCH? WHAT ARE YOU DOING HERE?
I'M WITH MY FAMILY. I JUST SAID.
WELL I'M WITH MY DEAR, DEAR FRIENDS, BONNIE!
I'M NOT GONNA SUDDENLY EAT WITH YOUR PROBABLY FAKE FAMILY OF ACTORS! NICE TRY!
UGH. I SHOULD KNOW BETTER AFTER THIRTY-TWO YEARS.
SEE YA, WINNIE.

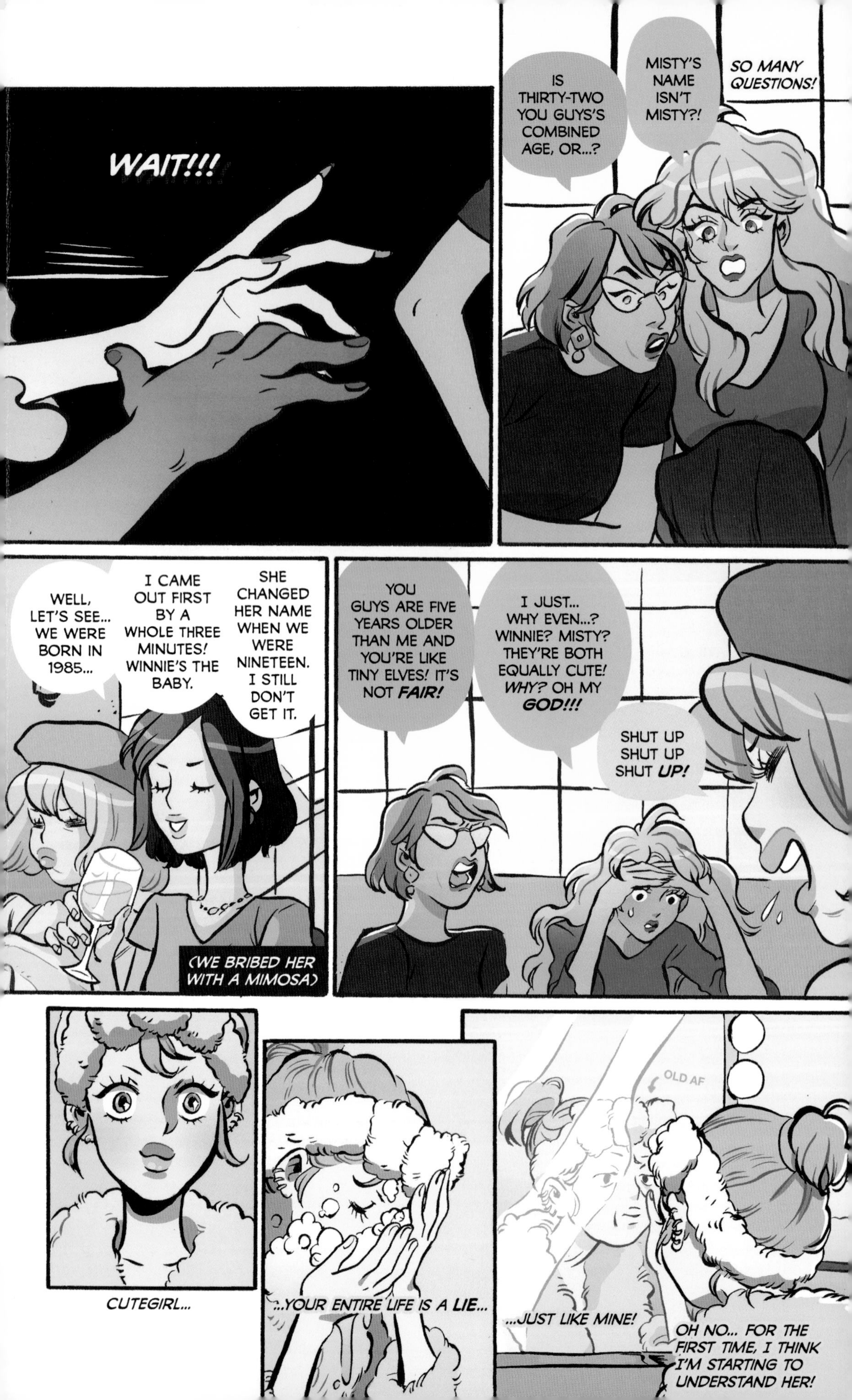
WAIT!!!
IS THIRTY-TWO YOU GUYS'S COMBINED AGE, OR...?
MISTY'S NAME ISN'T MISTY?!
SO MANY QUESTIONS!
WELL, LET'S SEE... WE WERE BORN IN 1985...
I CAME OUT FIRST BY A WHOLE THREE MINUTES! WINNIE'S THE BABY.
SHE CHANGED HER NAME WHEN WE WERE NINETEEN. I STILL DON'T GET IT.
(WE BRIBED HER WITH A MIMOSA)
YOU GUYS ARE FIVE YEARS OLDER THAN ME AND YOU'RE LIKE TINY ELVES! IT'S NOT FAIR!
I JUST... WHY EVEN...? WINNIE? MISTY? THEY'RE BOTH EQUALLY CUTE! WHY? OH MY GOD!!!
SHUT UP SHUT UP SHUT UP!
CUTEGIRL...
...YOUR ENTIRE LIFE IS A LIE...
OLD AF
...JUST LIKE MINE!
OH NO... FOR THE FIRST TIME, I THINK I'M STARTING TO UNDERSTAND HER!

I'M GOING HOME TO PLAN.
PLAN WHAT?
YOUR **DESTRUCTION!!**
AH, YES. GOOD LUCK WITH THAT.
WOW, SHE TOOK OFF IN A HURRY. I GUESS I WOULD TOO...
SOMETIMES I ENVY HER, YOU KNOW.

WHEN WE WERE SEVEN, WINNIE WANTED A PUPPY MORE THAN ANYTHING. SHE BEGGED AND PLEADED AND **PROMISED** SHE'D TAKE CARE OF HIM ALL BY HERSELF.
FINALLY MOM AND DAD GAVE IN.
WINNIE NAMED HIM, PUT SWEATERS ON HIM, BUT YOU KNOW WHAT...? AFTER TWO WEEKS, *I* WAS THE ONE STUCK FEEDING HIM AND PICKING UP HIS SH**
NOW HE *LIVES* WITH ME! WINNIE *ABANDONED* THAT DOG.

YOU KNOW... SHE'S A LITTLE BIT FLAKY.
JUST A LITTLE BIT!
FLAKY IS ONE THING.
I LIVE TWENTY MINUTES AWAY. SHE HASN'T VISITED IN ***SIX YEARS***.

SIX YEARS!
MAKES ME FEEL LIKE I SHOULD CALL MY SISTERS JUST TO SAY I LOVE THEM!
MAYBE SOME OTHER TIME...

Meet & Greet
(the following week)

UM, ARE YOU SIGNING THINGS...?
CAN YOU SIGN YOUR NYLON JAPAN PROFILE?*
IF I CAN JUST FIND IT...
*NYLON JAPAN, JUNE 2014
Couldn't read the text, but
I looked hot in the photo
slip

SPLUT

OH DANG!
HUH...
I GOT IT.

SOB I'M SO SORRY...
AWW, SHH, IT'S OKAY! ACCIDENTS HAPPEN EVERY DAY. IT'S NO BIGGIE!

I FEEL BAD FOR HER, BUT ALSO GLAD FOR HER BECAUSE I'M SO NICE!
DAB
DAB

HELLO, I'M VIRGIL! I'VE BEEN FOLLOWING YOUR WORK FOR QUITE SOME TIME.
YOU WERE IN LINE?! I THOUGHT YOU WORKED HERE! THANKS SO MUCH!
WHAT A LITTLE CUTIE...
I'M JUST GLAD I COULD HELP. YOU DON'T KNOW ME YET, BUT WE HAVE A MUTUAL... CAROLINE.
HUH??
CAROLINE?! OH, I DON'T-- I DON'T KNOW HER VERY WELL... ARE YOU TWO CLOSE?
ACTUALLY, I'M HER BROTHER.
SHE HAS A BROTHER?! GRANTED, I DON'T REALLY KNOW ANYTHING ABOUT CAROLINE...
...NOT HER TWIN BROTHER?

HAHA, NO! I'M THE BABY. CAN YOU SIGN THIS FOR ME?
THE BABY BROTHER WANTS ME TO SIGN SOMETHING?! I'M LIKE, WEIRDLY FLATTERED...
I WAS HAVING PRINTER TROUBLE.
tiny printout
...NEVER MIND!!!

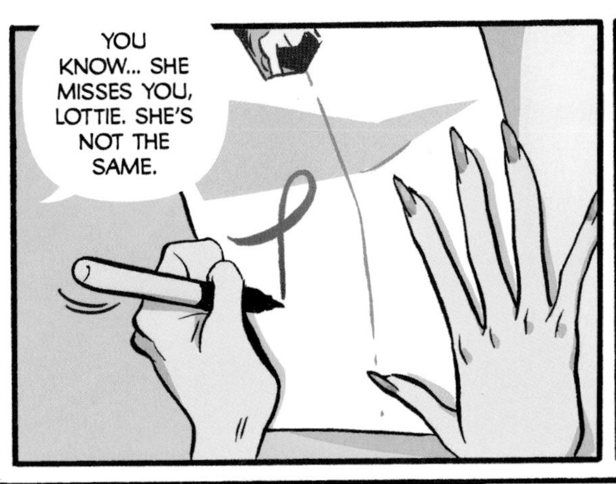
YOU KNOW... SHE MISSES YOU, LOTTIE. SHE'S NOT THE SAME.

I MISS HER TOO, BUT... IT'S *COMPLICATED*.

WHEN YOU TWO WERE FRIENDS, SHE WAS HAPPIER THAN I'D SEEN HER IN A *LOOOOOOOONG* TIME.
WHEN WE WERE FRIENDS, PEOPLE GOT ***HURT***. I DON'T NEED THAT IN MY LIFE.
UNDERSTATEMENT OF THE CENTURY, BUT I DON'T KNOW WHAT HE KNOWS...
*GOD, HE'S **SO** HOT. HE REALLY **IS** HER BROTHER! I CAN'T STOP LOOKING AT HIM!*

ALL I'M GONNA SAY IS, ***SHE'S HURTING TOO,*** LOTTIE.
DO A GOOD DEED AND TEXT HER, 'K? PEACE!

DANG IT! JUST WHEN I WAS DOING SO WELL WITH MY PLAN... NEVER THINKING ABOUT CAROLINE EVER AGAIN...
*WHAT DID HE SAY HIS NAME WAS-- **VIRGIN?** I MEAN **VIRGIL**?*

Cutegirl is here!
Only 57 minutes late!
THANKS FOR WAITING, Y'ALL... YOU KNOW I'M WORTH IT!
IT'S ABOUT TIME! WHAT'S WITH THE OUTFIT? DO YOU HAVE PINKEYE AGAIN?
I KNOW IT SOUNDS CUTE, BUT IT'S NOT.
I'LL BE THE JUDGE OF WHAT'S CUTE!!
WHATEVER YOU SAY, WINNIE!
RAHHHHHHHH!!
YOU CAN'T TRUST A WORD BONNIE SAYS! SHE'S UGLY AND HER KID IS UGLY... THEY'RE FROM THE UNCUTE SIDE OF THE FAMILY.
UNCUTE?! SHE'S YOUR IDENTICAL TWIN!
LOOK AT MY FACE!
IT'S BETTER. IT'S JUST A BETTER FACE.

YOU'RE SO HARD ON HER AND I DON'T GET IT! WHAT'D SHE DO?
DO? DID SHE SHOW YOU HER FAKE FINGER? DID SHE TELL YOU ABOUT THE CHIFFON CAKE? DID SHE MENTION SHE STOLE MY BABY?!
YOU MEAN THE BABY... IS YOURS?!
THE ONE YOU THINK IS UGLY?

NO, DUMMY!! MR. FLUFFY, MY OLD PUPPY FROM SWEET CHILDHOOD!
A HUMAN BABY?? EW.
BONNIE TOLD US YOU ABANDONED HIM! AND ALSO--

FWIP
--I KNEW IT!!

PINKEYE
DON'T ACT LIKE IT'S GROSS! I'M HERE, AREN'T I? I MADE PINKEYE WORK FOR ME. I ALWAYS MAKE IT WORK!
DAMN! THIS IS MAKING IT WORK?!
WHERE'S MY HAND SANI??

HOW DOES MISTY DO IT? ALL HER WORST ASPECTS MYSTERIOUSLY TURN INTO STRENGTHS!
THEY LOVE IT
THE UNIVERSE JUST DOESN'T MAKE SENSE...

Lately he's been getting antsy.
LAPD SPECIAL SECTION
DOWNTOWN PRECINCT
WHY ARE WE *DOING* THIS?!
SLAM
'CAUSE IT'S OUR ***JOB***, PARTNER. YOU FEELIN' ALRIGHT?

I THOUGHT OUR ***JOB*** WAS *PROTECTING THE INNOCENT*, NOT JUST IDLY KEEPING TABS ON *EVIL, UGLY* CAREER CRIMINALS!
HOW'D I KNOW YOU WERE GONNA SAY "UGLY"...?
HOW ABOUT THIS MISSING PERSON? HEAR ME OUT! SHE'S AN ***L.A. FASHION BLOGGER*** WHO ***MYSTERIOUSLY DISAPPEARED*** FROM A MOTEL IN THE DESERT--
FASHION BLOGGER? MAN, YOU GOTTA STOP DOING THE KEYWORD SEARCH.
YOU KNOW THE CHIEF REFERRED TO US AS THE *FASHION POLICE* IN FRONT OF MY ***WIFE***? I GOT *MAD* SIDE-EYE...

12:57 PM

SWIPE
AHH, LET'S BREAK FOR LUNCH.

THE INFAMOUS FASHION POLICE RIDE AGAIN!
WHAT DID I *JUST* SAY?

I MISSED YOU.
SO MUCH IT HURT.
IT TORE ME APART.
IT NEARLY
DESTROYED ME.

Downtown LA (Arts District)
1:15 PM
I COULDN'T GET THE DREAM OUT OF MY HEAD.
I'M SORRY, GOD... I TEXTED HER.
IT'S SO GOOD TO SEE YOU!
YEAH. SURE.
HUG
SO WHAT'S--
DON'T ACT LIKE YOU CARE.

I KNOW WE'RE ONLY MEETING BECAUSE OF *HIM*.
HUH?

YOU KNOW.
MY **COUSIN.**

YOU MEAN *VIRGIL?* ISN'T HE YOUR *BROTHER?*
OH. RIGHT. YEAH. MY BROTHER.
WHAT?! WHICH ONE IS IT?

CAROLINE, LOOK. I MAY NOT KNOW MUCH ABOUT YOU--
YOU DON'T KNOW THE *FIRST* THING ABOUT ME AND YOU DON'T *CARE*. YOU'RE A SHITTY FRIEND.
ME?! YOU'RE *THE ONE WHO-- UGH!!*

THAT'S NOT FAIR! YOU PUT ME IN A F**KED-UP SITUATION, SO YEAH, I *RAN!* AND NOW LOOK AT YOU. MAYBE YOU NEED A ***SHITTY FRIEND LIKE ME*** TO TELL YOU TO WASH YOUR FACE AND COMB YOUR HAIR!
WHO CARES WHAT I LOOK LIKE?

FASHION IS STUPID.

>:O

THIS ISN'T *YOU*, CAROLINE!
AT LEAST I SURE HOPE NOT...

YOU CAN'T ***BLAME*** YOURSELF FOR WHAT HAPPENED ON NEW YEAR'S. YOU KNOW IT WAS RULED AN *ACCIDENT*, RIGHT??
LISTEN. MY FRIENDS AND I HAVE THIS MONTHLY BRUNCH, AND YOU WOULD FIT RIGHT IN-- WE *LOVE* NEW PEOPLE--

HE'S WATCHING US RIGHT NOW, YOU KNOW. HE'S ALWAYS WATCHING.
VIRGIL? ***WHY***?

THEY DON'T TRUST ME TO BE ON MY OWN.

TIP

NOT AGAIN!!
HUH?

ANYONE NEED A TOWEL?
WHAT THE HELL?

WHAT IS HE, YOUR BUTLER?
I'M HER BROTHER AND I JUST LIKE TO BE USEFUL!
HE'S ALWAYS AROUND. ALWAYS WATCHING. ALWAYS CLEANING.

THAT'S RIDICULOUS. WOULDN'T I HAVE SEEN HIM BEFORE?

YOU HAVE.

THAT NIGHT IS HAZY, BUT I'M STARTING TO REMEMBER...
New Year's Day
4:10 AM

THE KID HELPING YOU--
--WAS HIM.

NEW YEAR'S. I SAW YOU TOGETHER AT THE CRIME SCENE. HOW'D I FORGET...?
NO... *EARLIER.*

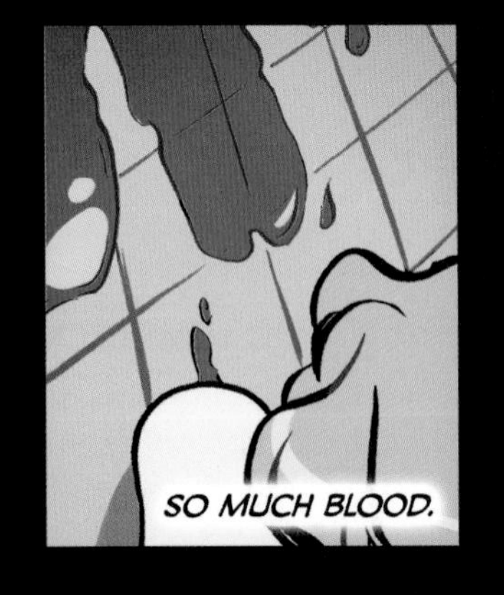
SO MUCH BLOOD.

WHO'S GOING TO...

...CLEAN THIS UP?

YEAH, THAT'S VIRGIL. SO *MEMORABLE.* SUCH A DELIGHT.
TO ANSWER YOUR QUESTION, ***YES...*** HE'S MY BUTLER.

I AM NOT!

tip

HIS WORD AGAINST MINE.
CLEANING

ANYWAY, WHERE WERE WE?
OH, RIGHT... SOMEBODY DIED.

Mr. FLUFFY
Our Old Baby
SEE? OLD DOG. NATURAL CAUSES. NOT MY FAULT.

SURPRISING EVERYONE, MISTY INVITED US GIRLS TO THE FUNERAL (IN BONNIE'S BACKYARD).
AND I GOTTA SAY...

...I'M GLAD I WORE WATERPROOF MASCARA.

I'M LEGIT PROUD OF HER!
IT REALLY DOES FEEL LIKE SHE'S TURNING OVER A NEW LEAF.
COLOR ME SHOCKED AS SH

FUNERAL CAKE, SIS?
JUST FROSTING FOR ME, PLEASE!
YOU TWO WERE SUCH CUTIE-PIES!
IT'S HONESTLY CREEPING ME OUT.
WAIT, HOW OLD WAS MR. FLUFFY? LIKE 25?
IS THAT NORMAL FOR A DOG?
The girls and Mr Fluffy Easter 1994
NO WAY IN HELL. MOM AND DAD REPLACED HIM AT LEAST TWICE. MR. FLUFFY WAS DEFINITELY A GIRL DOG FOR MOST OF THE 2000s.
MISTER FLUFFY IS AN ANGEL IN HEAVEN!
PERFECTLY WILLING TO LIVE IN DENIAL...
SO LIKE, WHY DID YOU GUYS STOP DRESSING THE SAME? WHAT HAPPENED?
I GUESS THERE CAME A TIME WHEN I DIDN'T WANT TO BE CUTE ANYMORE.
YEAH, BON, YOU CHANGED. YOU'RE A BORING GRANDMA NOW.
PEOPLE CAN CHANGE!
THIS PHOTO ALBUM PROVES IT!

ALL DOWNTOWN EXITS
THANKS FOR COMING! I PROMISE IT'S THE LAST TIME.
WITH MR. FLUFFY OUT OF THE PICTURE, I DON'T NEED TO VISIT BONNIE AGAIN UNTIL *SHE* DIES!

I GUESS WE ALL LEARNED NOTHING.
BUT WE HAD FUN AND DROVE SAFELY!

HEY, SO... YOU GUYS ARE *SURE* CAROLINE CAN COME TO BRUNCH?

I'D SURE BE FASCINATED TO MEET HER! I *ADORE* HER BLOG.
NOT A LOT OF UPDATES LATELY...
KEEP IT IN YOUR PANTS, MEG! *I* SAW HER BLOG FIRST!
HUH.
YOU KNOW WHAT...?

FOR THE FIRST TIME IN A LONG TIME...

...I FEEL LIKE, JUST MAYBE, THINGS ARE GOING TO BE OKAY.
YOU KNOW. IN A **COSMIC** SENSE.

210 likes · Liked by meganfoster
tieperson RIP MR FLUFFY
w all 370 comments
lore0 is mr fluffy ur boyfriend

SCROLL
SCROLL

SCROLL
SCROLL
CHARLENE L
COMA PATIENT
SINCE 1/1/2017

ANGELES PUBLIC LIBRARY
Name:
SUNNY DAY KIM
Sunny
HEY.
YOU'VE BEEN IN HERE A LOT LATELY, AND I HAVE TO ASK...
LIKE... IS *SUNNY DAY* YOUR REAL NAME?
Checkout Desk
HA, YEAH.
MAN, I'M COOPED UP IN HERE ALL WEEK. I SURE COULD USE A SUNNY DAY.
YOU WANNA GRAB A CUP OF COFFEE?
UH... SORRY, I JUST... I CAN'T.
SEE... I HAVE THIS GIRLFRIEND...
...AND SHE'S IN A *COMA.*
S-SO FREAKIN' ROMANTIC! THIS GUY'S THE DREAM!!
EXIT

07. NEW FACE

I HAVE A MILLION WORRIES, BUT RIGHT NOW THEY DON'T MATTER, 'CAUSE IT'S...
Caroline's First Haters' Brunch!
ELAPSED WAIT TIME: 30 MINUTES
SO THIS IS HATERS' BRUNCH, HUH?
YOU GUYS MUST REALLY LOVE WAITING IN LINES.
NO, I MEAN, IF YOU WANT TO GO TO THE HOT NEW PLACES, YOU EITHER HAVE TO GET INVITED OR WAIT A BIT...
AHEM. LOTTIE AND I HAD THIS DISCUSSION LAST BRUNCH, AND WE CONCLUDED THAT WAITING IN LINE IS PART OF THE FUN.
AND THEN I SAID YOU GUYS WERE STUPID, WHICH STILL HOLDS TRUE!

Fucking Finally!!
SO LIKE, WHAT'S EVEN SUPPOSED TO BE *GOOD* HERE, MEG?
I DON'T KNOW WHAT ANY OF THIS MEANS. WHAT THE F**K IS AMARANTH?
YELP SAYS THE YUZU BLOODY MARYS ARE BOMB!
DO THEY HAVE TINY MUFFINS? I WANT HALF OF ONE OF THOSE.

BLOODY MARY VERDICT:
TASTES *WEIRD.*
SIP

EWW, IT'S NASTY!
JEEEEZ! HOW CAN THEY EVEN CALL THIS A BLOODY MARY?
*IT'S HONESTLY **FINE!** WHY IS SHE ACTING LIKE THIS? WHEN DID COOLGIRL GET SO UNCOOL?*

MY DRINK IS GOOD! TRY IT!
PUSH

IT'S A VIRGIN MIMOSA!
THAT'S JUST ***ORANGE JUICE!***
*UGH, THEY'RE **SO** EMBARRASSING! THIS FRIENDTEGRATION IS NEVER GOING TO STICK!*

GOD...
...I CAN FEEL HER JUDGMENT BURNING INTO ME.
I DON'T NEED YOUR SCORN, CAROLINE! GOOD FOOD PHOTOS ARE AN ESSENTIAL PART OF MY BRAND!
SO HAVE YOU DECIDED WHETHER YOU'LL JOIN US IN SAN DIEGO THIS YEAR, LOTTIE?
SAN DIEGO? EW.
WHAT'S IN SAN DIEGO?
UGH. THIS ONE BLOGGER PUTS ON A BIG PARTY AFTER COMIC CON. IT'S JUST A ROOM FULL OF HOT PEOPLE PRETENDING TO BE NERDS.
IT'S STUPID.
UH, YOU WORKED ON YOUR QUOTE UNQUOTE STUPID COSTUME ALL YEAR!
DON'T LEAVE ME WITH MEG!!
YEAH, YOU CAN'T BACK OUT NOW, LOTTIE! IT'S A FIVE-YEAR TRADITION!
WELL, MAYBE WE SHOULD GET SOME NEW TRADITIONS!
I'M NOT GOING TO THE PARTY, AND I'M DEFINITELY NOT A NERD!

SO ABOUT CAROLINE...
UGHHH! CAN WE PLEASE JUST ENJOY OUR FROYO?
NOT UNTIL YOU ACKNOWLEDGE THAT YOUR NEW FRIEND SUCKS!
Post-brunch frozen yogurt (minus Caroline)
GUYS, OH MY GOD, SHE'S JUST GOING THROUGH SOME STUFF. SHE'LL WARM UP TO YOU. I *REALLY* WANT US ALL TO BE FRIENDS.
I SWEAR SHE'S GREAT! JUST TRUST ME!!
IS SHE THE ONLY ONE WHO'S *"GOING THROUGH SOME STUFF,"* LOTTIE?
ANYWAY, I *DO* LIKE HER. AND SHE'S *VERY* PRETTY.
IS SHE?
OH MY GOD, NOT THIS AGAIN.
IS SHE...?
1 new message
OH NO.
OH NO
OH NO
OH NO
Sunny - just now
Charlene woke up.

WHO IS SHE?
SHE'S A VERY LUCKY YOUNG LADY.
IF THAT TREE HADN'T BROKEN HER FALL, SHE'D BE FLAT AS A PANCAKE.
PANCAKE...?
I WANT ONE...
HEY DOC, CAN WE GET SOME PANCAKES SENT UP?
WE SURE CAN!
ANY OTHER REQUESTS, CHAR?
EGGS... SAUSAGES... BACON... OJ... MIXED TOAST...

WHEN DO THE BANDAGES COME OFF, DOC?

WON'T BE LONG NOW. THERE WAS EXTENSIVE DAMAGE, BUT THEY DON'T CALL ME THE BEST PLASTIC SURGEON IN THE SOUTHLAND FOR NOTHING!
I THINK YOU'LL BE VERY PLEASED.

I FEEL LIKE I'M LIVING IN A DREAM!
SUNNY, YOU WAITED FOR ME THIS WHOLE TIME?
DIDN'T SEEM SO LONG. GOT A LOT OF READING DONE...
GOD, YOU'RE INCREDIBLE, SUNNY...
AND YOU'RE MINE... ALL MINE...
SMILING LIKE THIS REALLY HURTS...
OH! YOU SHOULD SAY HI TO YOUR PARENTS!
PROUD OF YOU! HE'S A KEEPER! TALL!
WE SHOULD GET GOING! TRAFFIC!

WOW... AFTER ALL THESE YEARS...
MY DREAM... PLASTIC SURGERY... I'M FINALLY GOING TO BE AS PRETTY AS MY IDOL, LOTTIE PERSON!
...HUH.
GUESS SHE'S STILL A LITTLE LOOPY...

AFTER COOLGIRL BOMBED AT BRUNCH, I THOUGHT SHE'D GO INTO HIDING FOR WEEKS. INSTEAD, SHE INVITED ME OVER FOR THE FIRST TIME EVER.
SO WHAT THE HELL IS THIS PLACE? DOES SHE REALLY LIVE HERE? WHO LIVES IN THE HOLLYWOOD HILLS?
COOLGIRL... WHAT'S YOUR DEAL?
SO SHE WOKE UP FROM THE COMA, HUH?

GOOD FOR HER! GOOD JOB!
THAT'S ALL YOU HAVE TO SAY?!
WHAT THE HELL ARE YOU THINKING?
ARE YOU AT ALL CONCERNED ABOUT THE FACT...
...THAT WE WERE THE LAST PEOPLE CHARLENE SAW BEFORE SHE FELL?
WE PUSHED THIS POOR GIRL OFF A BUILDING AND SHE SURVIVED, SNOTTIE...

...ISN'T THAT A GOOD THING? CHILL! LET HER LIVE HER LIFE!
YOU PUSHED HER OFF A BUILDING. YOU.

A MILLION PEOPLE SAW HER DRUNK AS F**K AT THE PARTY. ZERO PEOPLE SAW WHAT HAPPENED.
AND BESIDES, SHE HAD IT COMING.
THAT'S SAVAGE!! DAMN... AM I GONNA BE THE NEXT PERSON SHE PUSHES OFF A ROOF? WE'RE PRETTY HIGH UP...

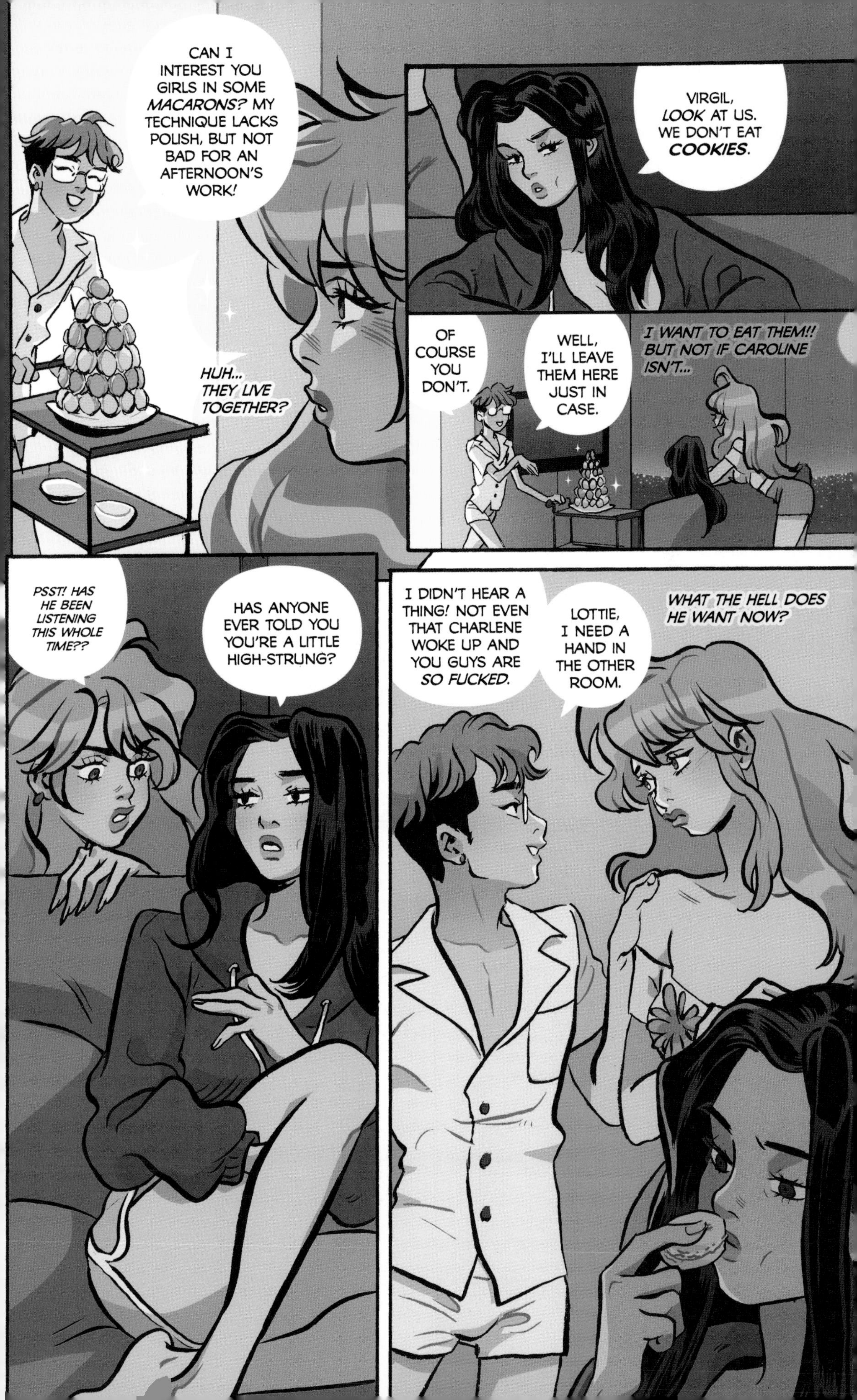
CAN I INTEREST YOU GIRLS IN SOME MACARONS? MY TECHNIQUE LACKS POLISH, BUT NOT BAD FOR AN AFTERNOON'S WORK!
HUH... THEY LIVE TOGETHER?
VIRGIL, LOOK AT US. WE DON'T EAT COOKIES.
OF COURSE YOU DON'T.
WELL, I'LL LEAVE THEM HERE JUST IN CASE.
I WANT TO EAT THEM!! BUT NOT IF CAROLINE ISN'T...
PSST! HAS HE BEEN LISTENING THIS WHOLE TIME??
HAS ANYONE EVER TOLD YOU YOU'RE A LITTLE HIGH-STRUNG?
I DIDN'T HEAR A THING! NOT EVEN THAT CHARLENE WOKE UP AND YOU GUYS ARE SO FUCKED.
LOTTIE, I NEED A HAND IN THE OTHER ROOM.
WHAT THE HELL DOES HE WANT NOW?

BROTHER? COUSIN? KEEPER? WHAT IS HE TO YOU? INSTEAD OF GETTING ANSWERS, I JUST HAVE MORE QUESTIONS...
HEY, VIRGIL, CAN I ASK YOU SOMETHING? IT'S... ABOUT CAROLINE.

ASK ME ANYTHING! BUT FIRST-- LOTTIE, *PLEASE* GO TO SAN DIEGO.
GET CAROLINE OUT OF THE CITY. IT'S A GREAT WAY FOR HER TO BOND WITH YOU GIRLS!

WHA--
WERE YOU LISTENING IN ON OUR BRUNCH?
YES.

HE STRAIGHT-UP ADMITS IT!!
GOD! VIRGIL! I DON'T LIKE BEING SPIED ON, OKAY?
OKAY.

I PROMISE I'LL NEVER SPY ON YOU AGAIN, LOTTIE. I'M GENUINELY SORRY FOR INFRINGING ON THE PRIVACY OF YOUR SANCTUARY, THE HATERS' BRUNCH.
PLEASE TAKE MY BIG SISTER TO SAN DIEGO AND HAVE FUN. GOD KNOWS SHE COULD USE IT IN THE TIME SHE HAS LEFT.

WAIT, *WHAT?*
THE TIME SHE HAS LEFT BEFORE *FASHION WEEK*. THERE'S NO TIME FOR FUN DURING *FASHION WEEK!*

WHAT DID HE MEAN? WHY ARE THESE TWO SO **DRAMATIC**?
THAT'S IT... I'M CONVINCED. THEY **HAVE** TO BE SIBLINGS.
DID YOU GUYS TALK ABOUT ME?
VIRGIL THINKS WE SHOULD GO TO SAN DIEGO THIS WEEKEND.

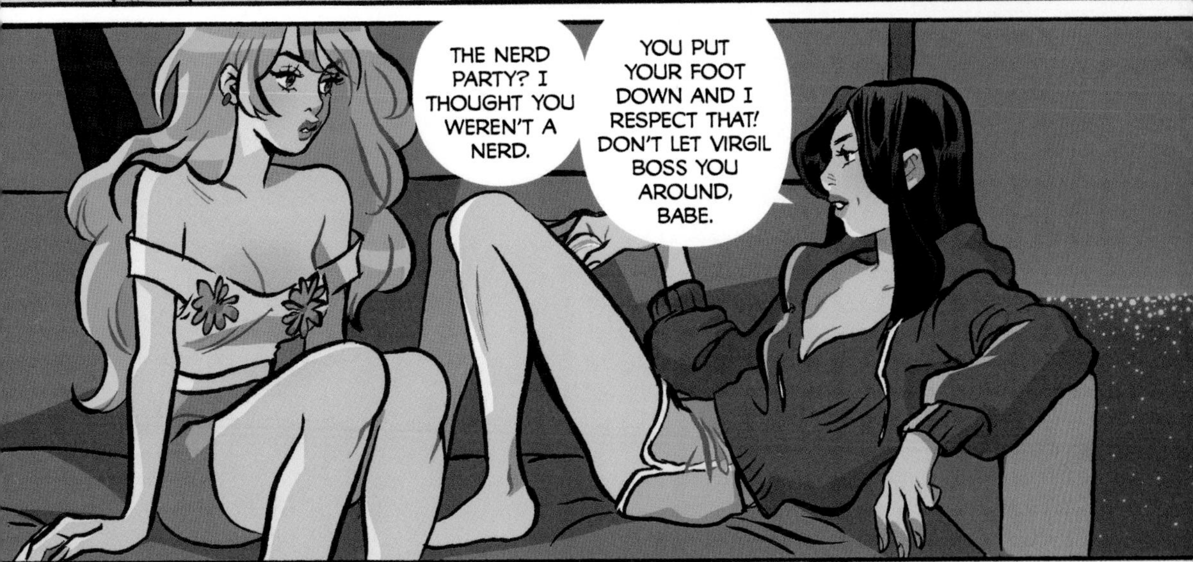
THE NERD PARTY? I THOUGHT YOU WEREN'T A NERD.
YOU PUT YOUR FOOT DOWN AND I RESPECT THAT! DON'T LET VIRGIL BOSS YOU AROUND, BABE.

WELL... I KINDA *DO* WANT TO GO. I JUST DIDN'T THINK IT'D BE YOUR THING. IT FELT UNCOOL. I'M SORRY! I WAS BEING AN INSECURE IDIOT!

NOT MY THING? IT'S A ***PARTY***, RIGHT? THAT'S IT, WE'RE GOING.
GIRLS' TRIP TO SAN DIEGO!! WOO!

The macarons...
WHAT? YOU GUYS WERE GONE FOR A *WHILE*.

THE DESERT.
SHE MADE STARTER, MAN. POINT GUARD. I KNOW IT'S JUST MIDDLE SCHOOL, BUT I'M DAMN PROUD.
AND HOW'S YOUR SON?

EHH... HE JOINED A *QUIDDITCH* LEAGUE.
OHH... SO... HE'S FLYING ON A BROOM?

NO, JOHN, MY BOY IS NOT FLYING. IT'S A FAKE-ASS, HARRY POTTER-ASS SPORT. MY BOY'S A *NERD.*

WELL, NERDS ARE SMART, RIGHT? MAYBE HE'LL GO INTO *AEROSPACE ENGINEERING.*
MAYBE HE'LL LEAD THE EFFORT TO COLONIZE *MARS!* FROM BROOMSTICKS TO ***MARS,*** ABE!

JOHN... YOU SAID WE WERE GOING OUT FOR LUNCH. WHERE THE HELL ARE WE, MAN? WHAT HAPPENED TO THE BEST PATTY MELT IN THE SOUTHLAND?
IT'S COMING! WE JUST HAVE TO MAKE *ONE QUICK STOP.*

REMEMBER THE FASHION BLOGGER WHO DISAPPEARED? THAT *MOTEL* IS RIGHT AROUND HERE!
COMPLETE COINCIDENCE! ISN'T THAT *WILD*, ABE?
WHY'D I LET YOU DRIVE...?

IT'S WHAT?!
TORE DOWN. THEY'RE TURNIN' IT INTO SOME KINDA *HIP, BOO-TIQUE* HOTEL. I HEAR WE'RE GETTIN' A CHIPOTLE®, TOO!

ALRIGHT. WE'RE HEADING STRAIGHT BACK AFTER LUNCH, AND *I'M* DRIVING. CHIEF'S GONNA BE PISSED WE TOOK OFF FOR NO REASON.
24 HRS
Diney's
DINER
NO REASON?

THERE'S *SOMETHING* GOING ON HERE, ABE.
YOU GOTTA DROP THIS FASHION POLICE THING, JOHN. WE HAVE CASES WAITING BACK HOME!

WELL, WELL, *WELL,* WELL, ***WELL.*** WOULD YOU GET A LOAD OF THE CITY BOYS.
Y'ALL ENJOYIN' YOUR MEAL?

YOU HOMOS DRIVE ALL THE WAY OUT HERE 'CUZ ***YELP*** SAID SO?

FWP

N-NOT THAT THERE'S ANY-THING WRONG WITH *YELP*, OFFICER!
P-P-PLEASE DON'T PUNISH US BY LEAVING A NEGATIVE REVIEW FOR THIS ESTABLISHMENT! ONE NEGATIVE REVIEW CAN HAVE A DEVASTATING IMPACT ON A SMALL BUSINESS!

I'M EARLY...
HUH, I GUESS THAT'S HER PHYSICAL THERAPIST...
IS THIS NORMAL OR IS THIS WEIRD? I CAN'T REALLY TELL...
CAN YOU TAKE ME DOWNTOWN TOMORROW, SUNNY? THE THERAPIST GAVE ME A GOOD IDEA.
DOWNTOWN? ARE YOU SURE YOU'RE UP TO IT?
SHE'S ALREADY ASLEEP...

ARE YOU GOING TO CHANGE WHEN WE GET THERE? WHERE'S YOUR OUTFIT?
THIS *IS* MY OUTFIT.
GIRLS' TRIP (2017)
GOD, WHY DID I THINK THESE SHOES WERE A GOOD IDEA? WE *SHOULD* GET CHANGED DOWN THERE.
IT'S NOT THAT LONG OF A DRIVE, AND WE NEED TO MAKE AN *ENTRANCE*, GIRL!
YOU'RE WEARING ***FLATS.***
THEY'RE IN CHARACTER!

AND AWAYYY WE GO!
San Diego
100 miles
OOH, ALMOST FORGOT TO START THE MUSIC!
I MADE A THREE-HOUR PLAYLIST OF INSPIRATIONAL BANGERS, BUT OF COURSE I'M OPEN TO SUGGESTIONS!
I ONLY LISTEN TO FIFTEENTH-CENTURY OPERA.

OOH... I THINK I SAW SOME GREGORIAN CHANTS ON SPOTIFY...
SHE'S *JOKING*, MEG.
HAHA... OBVI...

Misty: huh weird i cant remember when we all voted to let boring girl join us on our beautiful traditional trip
when was that

SNATCH
GIVE ITTTT!

THIS IS THE SPOT.
IT WAS HERE THAT I FELL.
CAUTION
CAUTION
THIS IS WHERE YOU FELL!
20 feet away
SUNNY...
I'M SORRY I WASN'T HERE TO CATCH YOU.

IT'S ALL JUST **BLANK** TO ME.
WHO LEFT THIS HERE?
POKÉ
NEW!
I DON'T REMEMBER THIS.
WHAT DOES IT ALL MEAN?
I KNOW THIS PLACE.
WE CAME IN LAST SUMMER. PRETTY GOOD BEER LIST.
WHY ARE WE HERE, CHAR?
...IS IT HELPING YOU REMEMBER?
...NO. I JUST HAVE TO PEE.

SOMETHING HAPPENED HERE.
THERE'S SOMETHING AWFUL BEHIND THIS DOOR.

EXIT

I...
HAVE...
TO...
PEEEEEEE!
CHILDREN! WHAT DO YOU WANT FROM ME?
WHO KNEW THERE'D BE SO MUCH TRAFFIC EN ROUTE TO COMIC CON? WE'RE ALL ITCHY AND SWEATY AND DISGUSTING!
DAMN, SPEAK FOR YOURSELF! I'M A PRINCESS WHO HAS TO PEE!
THIS IS YOUR CAR, MEG! WHY'S THE AC BUSTED?!
DIDN'T HONDA SPRING FOR A SERVICE PACKAGE WHEN THEY GAVE YOU THE SPONSORSHIP? I DIDN'T EVEN WANT TO GO TO THIS PARTY AND NOW I'M GONNA DIE BY DROWNING IN MISTY'S PEE!
SH-SHUT UP!!

OH, FOR HEAVEN'S SAKE, LOTTIE, STOP ACTING COOL!
YOU LOVE WAITING IN LINES, BEING STUCK IN TRAFFIC, GOING TO PARTIES WITH PEOPLE YOU HATE...
YOU LOVE SUFFERING!
OH MY GOD! THAT MUST BE WHY I'M FRIENDS WITH YOU GUYS!
I GIVE UP! I'M TURNING AROUND AS SOON AS I CAN DO SO SAFELY! SAN DIEGO IS CANCELLED!
SOB

YOUR FRIENDS ARE *SO FUNNY,* SNOTTIE!
WE'RE MOVING! THANK THE LORDE!
FASTER! I STILL HAVE TO PEE!!

S-SNOTTIE?!?

THEY WEREN'T PAYING ATTENTION, RIGHT? NOBODY HEARD THAT.
GOD... NEARLY HAD A HEART ATTACK...
EXIT UP HERE!

BEST GAS STATION BATHROOMS IN THE SOUTHLAND! DON'T SAY I NEVER DID ANYTHING FOR YA!

CLOP
CLOP
CLOP
CLOP
KLONK
BAREFOOT?? *DISGUSTING!* YOU ARE *NOT* ALLOWED BACK IN THE CAR!!

FINALLY.
I FINALLY GOT TO PEE...

HUH... CAROLINE SURE SEEMS CHIPPER NOW. I GUESS **THAT'S** GOOD.

LOOKS LIKE SHE AND MEG ARE GETTING ALONG...
I WONDER IF THEY'RE TALKING ABOUT ME.
WAIT, WHAT IF THEY **ARE?!** OH **GOD!** WHAT HAVE I DONE?

OKAY...
CUTE...
I'M NOT JEALOUS...
MEG WAS REAL UPSET, BUT BORING GIRL FIXED HER. GUESS SHE'S GOT HER USES...
DID YOU WASH YOUR HANDS? LET ME CHECK.

AND WE'RE BACK ON THE ROAD WITH A MILLION SNACKS.
MAYBE THIS FRIENDTEGRATION IS GONNA WORK OUT AFTER ALL!

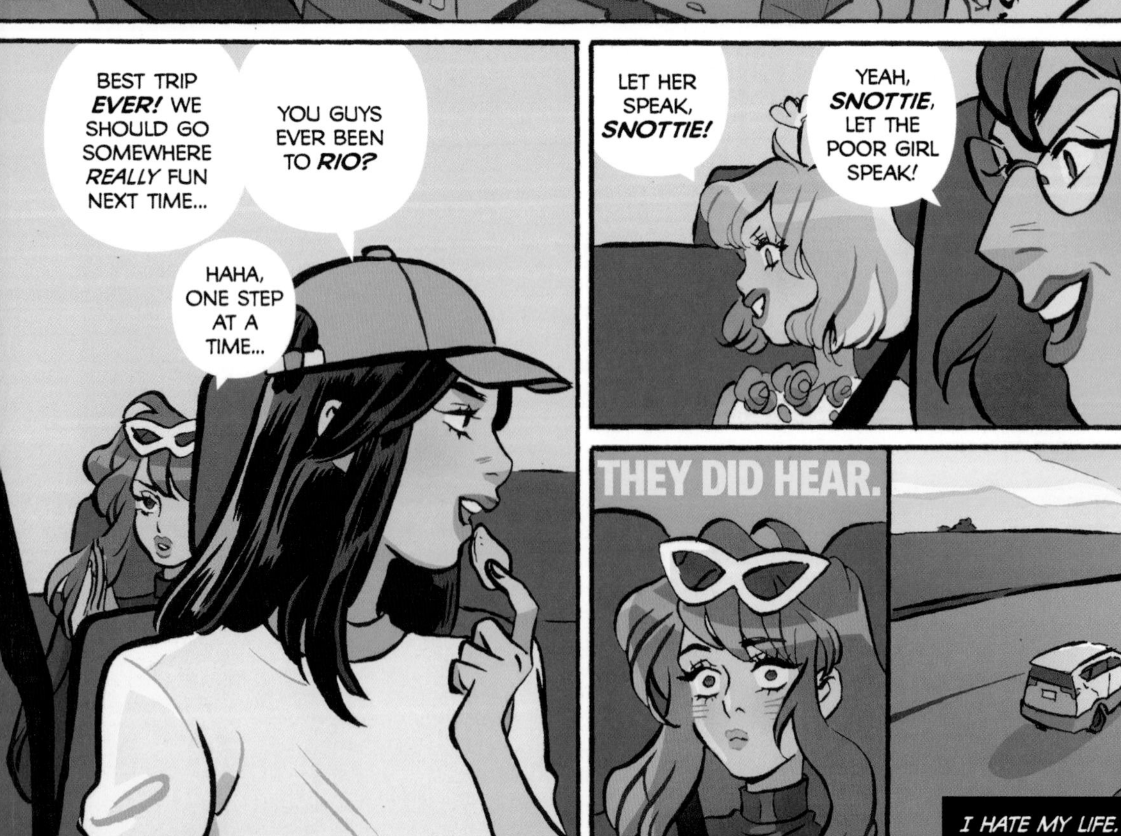
BEST TRIP EVER! WE SHOULD GO SOMEWHERE REALLY FUN NEXT TIME...
YOU GUYS EVER BEEN TO RIO?
HAHA, ONE STEP AT A TIME...
LET HER SPEAK, SNOTTIE!
YEAH, SNOTTIE, LET THE POOR GIRL SPEAK!
THEY DID HEAR.
I HATE MY LIFE.

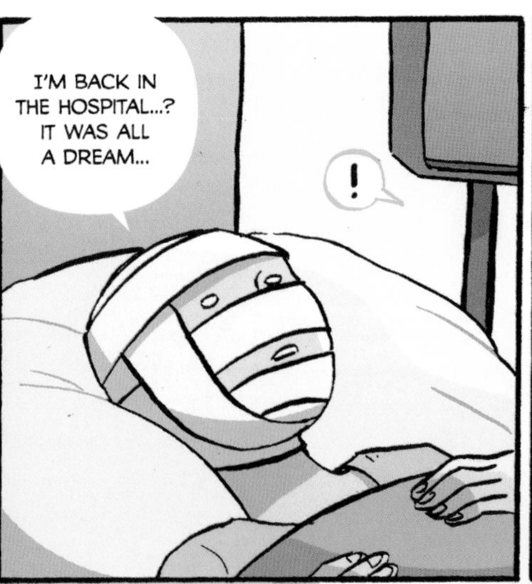
I'M BACK IN THE HOSPITAL...? IT WAS ALL A DREAM...
!

IT WASN'T A DREAM. YOU'VE BEEN OUT FOR THREE DAYS!

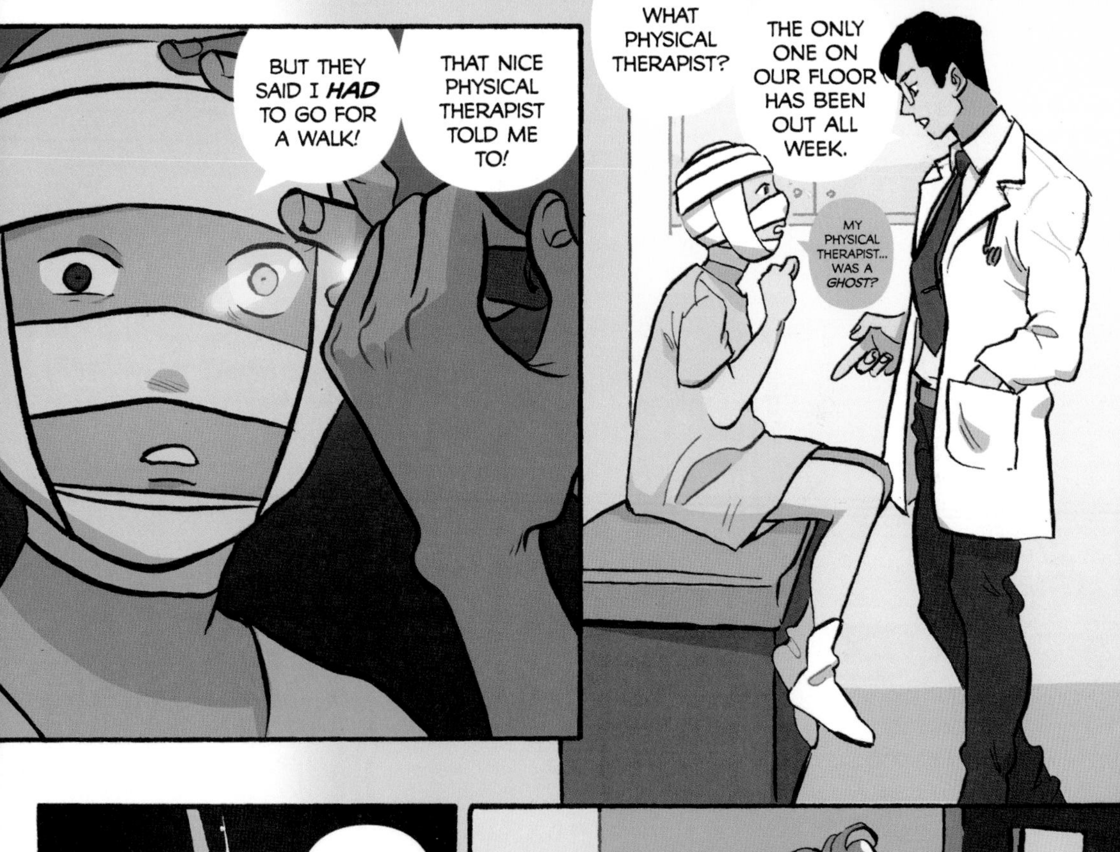
BUT THEY SAID I ***HAD*** TO GO FOR A WALK!
THAT NICE PHYSICAL THERAPIST TOLD ME TO!
WHAT PHYSICAL THERAPIST?
THE ONLY ONE ON OUR FLOOR HAS BEEN OUT ALL WEEK.
MY PHYSICAL THERAPIST... WAS A *GHOST?*

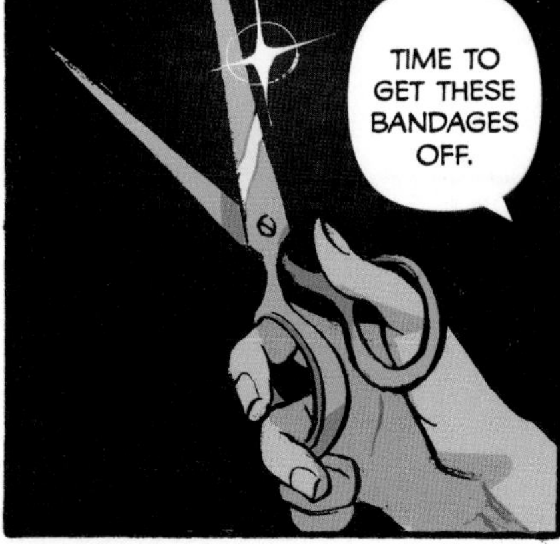
TIME TO GET THESE BANDAGES OFF.

JOT JOT

DON'T DO IT!!
WE WORKED SO HARD!!
YOU HAVE TO START OVER!!

I'M SORRY.
I'M OKAY NOW.
I AM.

OKAY! WELL! GEEZ...

C'MON, CHAR...
YOU'RE BEAUTIFUL JUST AS YOU ARE!

...

LET GO! HE LIKED ME BETTER IN BANDAGES!!
NO!
PLEASE!!

08. BOYS KEEP SWINGING
THE BABY IS COMING!
SHE'S PERFECT. JUST LIKE HER MOTHER.
snif
I'VE NEVER BEEN...
LICK
...SO HAPPY!!
DING!
You have 1 event today

SO THAT'S ME...
HOW ABOUT YOU GUYS? BIG PLANS?
JUST GONNA GET TO KNOW MY NEW ROOMIE CHARLENE!
DID YOU KNOW A LOT OF GIRLS ARE AFRAID TO LIVE ON THE GROUND FLOOR BECAUSE OF MURDERS? WELL, NOT ME AND CHARLENE!
HAHA, YEAH...

...BUT THERE'RE ALSO MANY *ADVANTAGES* TO LIVING ON THE GROUND FLOOR!!

PUSH
LOTTIE...

HEY... YOU'RE GONNA SPACKLE THAT HOLE WHEN SHE MOVES OUT, RIGHT?

I'LL BE SURE TO DO THAT.
ALRIGHT, CHAR, I GOTTA MEET UP WITH ASHLEY. TEXT ME IF YOU NEED ANYTHING!
ASHLEY? DO I KNOW HER?

AHH... ASHLEY'S A ***GUY***. MEG'S FIANCÉ, REMEMBER? HE'S WEIRD AND DUMB? SHE'S FORCING ME TO HANG OUT WITH HIM.

OH YEAH.
OKAY, BYE.

To: Ashley
Heading to the sports club.
HELL YEAH! Reserved my fav court, it's ON! 😈

THE SQUASH COURT.
OH BOY.
I WATCHED A COUPLE OF HOW-TOS ON YOUTUBE, BUT THIS DUDE DRESSES LIKE A PRO!
MAYBE I GOOFED...
ALRIGHT, LET'S HAVE SOME GOOD CLEAN FUN!
whif
AAHHH, SORRY!
NEVER MIND...
HE'S JUST RICH.
OOPS!

2ND TRY!
SMAAASH!!!

pok
POINT:
ASHLEY
ALREADY KICKIN' YOUR ASH!
DID YOU SAY MY *ASH?* THAT WAS *TERRIBLE.*

OH, YOU LIKE THAT?
'CUZ I GOT MORE!

BUT...
WOK

POINT:
SUNNY

SO HOW'S THE LIFE OF A CAMERA BOY? PHOTO GUY?
IT'S CALLED A PHOTOGRAPHER, IDIOT!!!
NOTHING BUT WEDDINGS LATELY. KINDA BORING... SPEAKING OF WHICH, WHEN'S YOURS?
YOU STILL WANT ME TO SHOOT IT?
NOT MY DEPARTMENT, BRO! THAT'S ALL MEG.
OF COURSE! TYPICAL!
BAP!
WHUP
YOU READY TO GET MARRIED, ASHLEY?
I'M DOWN TO COMMIT, BUT--
YOU KNOW THAT GREEN-HAIRED GIRL? GREENHAIR?
LOTTIE?
...YEAH... I KNOW HER...
WELL, I'M NO CHEATER, BUT I MIGHT NEED ONE LAST FREE BANG AT THE WEDDING.
AND IF IT'S GOTTA HAPPEN, GREENHAIR'S MY FIRST CHOICE! FOR ONE THING, SHE'S ALREADY SEEN MY ZORD.

HIS ZORD?!
HIS...
THOP
...ZORD?!
PKOW!
CAN'T THIS GUY KEEP HIS ZORD TO HIMSELF?!
DAMN, SUNNY!

SNAP
CALIFOR
ORNIA
DRIVER
KIM
SUNNY DAY
LASS C
6969 6969 6969 6969
04/20
SUNNY DAY
0000 0000 0000 0001
09/20
SUNNY KIM
EXPRESS
BUSINESS
1337 800757 58008
S.DAY, LLC
SNAP
SNAP
KLUNK

BAM!
plip

LET'S SHOWER AND THEN HIT THE SAUNA! THE SAUNA IS EVERYTHING, MAN.
ANYTHING'S BETTER THAN *SQUASH*. AT LEAST WE WORKED UP A SWEAT.
HAHAHA! YOU'RE JUST BITTER CUZ I WON!
UH, WE BOTH WON EQUAL SETS-- NOT THAT I CARE...
SO YOU DON'T MIND A VICTORY PIC?
SAY ***CHEESE!***
SNAP!

WHAT?! LET ME SEE!
AAAAAAAAND POSTED! WHEN YOU NOTICE AN INCREASE IN HOT LOCAL B*TCHES FOLLOWING YOU, REMEMBER THE REASON IS *ME*.
'CUZ A LOT OF MY FOLLOWERS ARE HOT LOCAL B*TCHES.

WHAT DID YOU POST?!

sports club wit my bro @sdayphotos! good dude even tho he suck at squash! Lol
WHAT THE...?

WAS THERE A *DELIVERY GUY* IN HERE?
WHY? YOU EXPECTING A PACKAGE? ...CUZ I GOT ONE RIGHT HERE! HAHA! IT'S HUGE!
C'MON, LET'S HIT THE SHOWERS.
THE HELL WAS THAT...?

SO HERE'S MY ADVICE TO YOU... DATE SOMEONE HOT!
YOU GOT THE STUFF, MAN.
THANKS, BUT I'M ALREADY SEEING SOMEONE...
HOW DOES HE FUNCTION?
HE LITERALLY HASN'T STOPPED TALKING ABOUT SEX THIS ENTIRE TIME...

BRO, THAT'S EXACTLY WHAT I'M SAYING! YOU COULD HAVE SO MUCH MORE.
I BET B*TCHES WANT TO CLIMB YOU LIKE A TREE EVERY DAY AND YOU IGNORE 'EM!

MEG'S MARRYING THIS GUY. I CAN HANDLE A FEW HOURS. HE'S NOT SO BAD.
DUDE, WAIT! YOU SHOULD BANG GREEN-HAIR AT MY WEDDING!
THEN LATER WE CAN WIFE SWAP!!

ACHOOO!

SNFFF

DIDN'T EVEN GET A HATERS' BRUNCH THIS MONTH.

CUTEGIRL'S IN STUPID TOKYO AGAIN WORKING ON HER SECRET PROJECT...

Meg: I love your friend Caroline! LOL
hey meg
found this pic of you
LOL. That's me?
here's another one
WHAT THE HELL, CAROLINE!!!!

YOU TEXT STUPID STUFF TO NORMGIRL?! WHY HER??

IT'S NOT FAIR.

RAAA
AAAH
RRAH

To: Caroline
jk i don't miss u!!!

To: Sunny
heyyyyy
having fun w/ ashley von freakazoid?
u guys talking abt me??

UGHHH... TEXT ME BACK!! WHO ELSE DO I EVEN KNOW?
JOHN CHO?!
OH... RIGHT... THAT DETECTIVE.

To: John
wyd?
INSTANT REPLY.
Nothing important. what's up?
YIKES... NEEDY...
TOSS

WHAM!

READ HIM HIS RIGHTS, ABE.
YOU HAVE THE RIGHT TO REMAIN SILENT!

DING!
wyd?
ANYTHING YOU SAY CAN AND WILL BE USED AGAINST YOU IN A COURT OF LAW!

Typing...
Nothing important. What's up?
YOU HAVE THE RIGHT TO AN ATTORNEY-- JOHN?!

SORRY, SORRY! I'M SPACEY TODAY...
JESUS! I'LL BRING THIS GUY IN. GET OUTTA HERE. TAKE A WALK.

TRY A SWIM AT THE SPORTS CLUB! ALWAYS CLEARS MY HEAD.
SHUT THE F**K UP!
SHE HASN'T REPLIED...

...WE HAVEN'T *YET*, BUT MEG SAYS SHE WANTS TO TRY NEW THINGS AFTER WE'RE MARRIED...
CAN YOU TONE DOWN THE SMUT LEVEL? SOMEONE'S COMING IN.

HUH...!
HOW ABOUT THAT! *SUNNY KIM?*

SUP, JOHN. LONG TIME. THIS IS MY FR--
...THIS IS ASHLEY!
YO!

GOOD OL' *SUNDAY SUNNY.*
'CAUSE WE MET BACK IN SUNDAY SCHOOL!

YEP... LONG TIME AGO...

SO!
WHAT'S Y'ALL'S ***KINK?*** MINE'S FOR SOME MODEL-LOOKING CHICK TO DRESS ME UP IN HER CLOTHES AND PEG ME IN THE BUNGHOLE!
.....

MY MOM STILL GIVES ME UPDATES ON YOUR CAREER, YOU KNOW.
TOLD ME YOU MADE DETECTIVE.
OH RIGHT, THEY GO TO THE SAME SPA... THAT'S HILARIOUS!
WHAT THE EFF, YOU GUYS DON'T HAVE ***KINKS?*** UNLESS *MILFS* ARE YOUR THING...

C'MON, ASHLEY-- NOT EVERYONE HAS ***KINKS!***

WELLLLLLLL...

I DON'T KNOW IF YOU'D CALL IT A KINK...
...BUT IF THERE'S ONE WEIRD THING THAT TURNS ME ON, IT'S ***GREEN HAIR!***

H-HEY!
WE KNOW SOMEONE YOU SHOULD BANG!!
ALSO: NOT REALLY A KINK, BUT IMA LET IT SLIDE...

OH, NO, NO... THAT'S NOT NECESSARY!

THIS CHICK'S HAIR IS GREEN AS HELL, DUDE! SUNNY WAS THINKING OF BANGING HER AT MY WEDDING, BUT NOW SHE'S ALL YOURS! RIGHT, SUNNY?
DAMN, SUNNY, FIRM QUADS. WHAT DO YOU SQUAT?

HER NAME IS LOTTIE, AND SHE'S A HUMAN BEING! YOU CAN'T JUST PIMP HER OUT...
...TO STRANGE MEN!!
I'M NOT... UH... STRANGE...
I THINK I KNOW HER.

YOU SHOULD BE DOING SOME SERIOUS SOUL-SEARCHING, ASHLEY.
YOU'RE ABOUT TO GET MARRIED, MAN!
WELL YOU SHOULD BE DOING SOME SERIOUS HUMPING! WE ALL KNOW YOUR GIRL DIED, BUT IT'S TIME TO MOVE ON TO GREENER PASTURES!

SHE DIDN'T DIE! SHE'S FINE! SHE'S JUST MILDLY SUICIDAL AND SO AM I BECAUSE I HAVEN'T HAD SEX IN EIGHT MONTHS!
SUNNY...
...I'M PRETTY SURE SHE F**KING DIED.

SHE ALMOST DID DIE, DUDE. I WAS THERE THAT NIGHT. LATER I HEARD THE REST OF THE STORY THROUGH THE MOM GRAPEVINE... SUNNY STAYING BY HER SIDE...
YOU WERE THERE FOR HER. YOU'RE A GOOD MAN.
I DON'T KNOW WHAT A GOOD MAN IS.
I JUST WANT TO LOVE AND BE LOVED. IS THAT SO CRAZY?
I DON'T THINK SO.
IF WE CAN GET BACK TO THE MATTER AT HAND...
...I THINK IT'S GAME ON, BRO! IF YOUR CHICK DIDN'T DIE, WE CAN JUST FOCUS ON GETTING JOHN HERE TO HOME BASE WITH GREENHAIR!
GET YOUR HANDS OFF ME, YOU FILTHY PIECE OF--

HNNGH
RAAGH
HURF

ALRIGHT, YOU'RE DONE! YOU GUYS ARE DONE! GOD, PULL IT TOGETHER.
OUR...
...TOWELS...

I'M SORRY, DUDE! NO HARD FEELINGS, MAN!
AGHH!

HARD FEELINGS? WHAT'S UP WITH YOUR ZORD?!?

AHHHHH, SORRY, MAN! DIDN'T GET A CHANCE TO RUB ONE OUT BEFORE I LEFT THE HOUSE!
YOU KNOW HOW ZORDS ARE...

...SO YEAH. HOW WAS *YOUR* DAY?
PRETTY GOOD!
I WATCHED ELEVEN EPISODES OF *GREY'S ANATOMY.*
COOL... I WAS KINDA ASKING CHARLENE, THOUGH...
MEGAN + ASHLEY
THIS WHAT YOU'VE BEEN UP TO ALL DAY?
YEP.

COOL! WHAT... UH... WHAT IS IT?

YOU'LL SEE.
HAHA... UM, OKAY! I'LL HOLD ON UNTIL THE BIG REVEAL!
JUST GLAD YOU'RE KEEPING BUSY.
HOW 'BOUT A GOOD-NIGHT KISS?

Smewp
WAIT A SEC! I JUST HAD A BRILLIANT THOUGHT.

YEAH... I WAS RIGHT! THIS CHANGES EVERYTHING... THIS IS HUGE! WOW!!
SUNNY...?
It's 3 AM...
PAGING DOCTOR... UH... GREY? I DON'T KNOW WHAT THIS SHOW IS ABOUT...
THEY'RE PAGING ME. I GOTTA GO.

1 new message
3 AM...
SUNNY...?
having fun w/ ashley von freakazoid?
u guys talking abt me??
Hahaha wow
Is that all you ever think about?
yea
duh!!
Stupid question, I guess.
i mean... tbh sometimes i think about...
you
Oh really?
and ashley
wrestling
w/ ur dicks out!!!!!
NOOOO! Who told you?
ur old friend john cho but he didn't tell me enoughhhhh
i need details! spill!!!
Oh geez. You know John, too?

Well, the first thing you need to know about Ashley is that he has a special name for his you-know-what...
NO
NOOOOOOOOOO
tell me
I'll tell you.
...but only if you tell me what you're wearing.
•••
u realize it's 3 am
Yeah, but this is YOU.
LOL
ok i'll tell u what i'm wearing but only bc i look hot and someone needs to know, ok?
It's a deal.

09. WEEKEND, PART 1: WALKING WITH A GHOST

Tokyo was cold.

As cold as ice cream...

...as cold as my soul.

When out of the blue...

...I met YOU.

[upbeat music playing]

WHISPER WHISPER

WHAT THE HELL IS GOING ON?

HOW LONG IS THIS SUPPOSED TO BE?

43 MINUTES LATER

THANK YOU TO THE FESTIVAL FOR HOSTING THE WORLD PREMIERE OF MY FIRST FILM, *TOKYO CITY TWINSIES.*
IT WAS SHOT ON LOCATION IN 2017 WITH MY FRIENDS IN TOKYO WHO YOU GUYS PROBABLY DON'T KNOW. QUESTIONS?
FIN.
Q&A with Misty Sutton
writer, director,
producer & star

DID YOU SHOOT THIS USING AN ACTUAL TWIN?

NO, SILLY. WHAT YOU SAW WAS MOVIE MAGIC! BOTH CHARACTERS WERE PLAYED BY MYSELF.
THIS IS A WORK OF FICTION, BASED ON MY LIFELONG DESIRE TO HAVE A TWIN SISTER.
Misty

BUT IN A 2012 REDDIT AMA YOU MENTIONED THAT YOU ***DO*** HAVE A TWIN SISTER.
COULDN'T YOUR ACTUAL TWIN HAVE PLAYED THE TWIN?
FIN.
WHERE'D SHE GO...?

SO GOOD! AND YOU LOOKED SO PRETTY! BOTH OF YOU!
IT WAS COOL.
FOR ME IT WAS A LITTLE LONG AND I JUST KEPT WONDERING WHEN SOMETHING WAS GOING TO HAPPEN.
I'LL KILL YOUR ASS!

A FEW YEARS AGO, SOME OF THE BIG BRANDS GOT TOGETHER TO PUT ON AN ANNUAL FESTIVAL FOR US INFLUENCERS. THEY CALL IT...
THANKSTRAVAGANZA
at the desert rose by valhalla
THANKSTRAVAGANZA! WE FINALLY GOT INVITED! FEELS LIKE WE'RE PART OF SOMETHING BIG, Y'KNOW?
INFLUENCER REGISTRATION
HOTEL CHECK-IN
FRIDAY

YEAH, A BIG PILE OF TOTAL CRAP!
DON'T YOU MEAN CRAPSTRAVAGANZA? YOU GIRLS HAVE FUN... I'M JUST HERE TO DRINK TEQUILA IN THE HOT TUB.

OH, CAROLINE, DON'T FORGET MY PRESENTATION ON SUNDAY!
"PLANNING THE PERFECT WEDDING!"

UGH...
REALLY?

WHAT?
NOTHING!
GREAT TITLE.

GO ON! SAY IT! "SHE'S NOT EVEN MARRIED! WHAT DOES SHE KNOW ABOUT THE PERFECT WEDDING?"

I'M SURE WE'LL FIND OUT ON SUNDAY!

I CAN'T EVEN FOCUS ON TALKING SHIT ABOUT MEG RIGHT NOW.
ABOUT TO CHECK IN TO THIS GORGEOUS BOUTIQUE HOTEL WITH CAROLINE BY MY SIDE...
I'VE WAITED SO LONG FOR THIS WEEKEND!!
EXCUSE ME, IS THIS THE LINE FOR INFLUENCER REGISTRATION, OR...?
UMM... I THINK THIS IS THE LINE FOR HOTEL CHECK-IN.
OHHH...
...WAIT, ARE YOU LOTTIE PERSON?
Y-YES! HI!
OH MY GOD!! YOU'RE LIKE THE BEST EVER! CAN WE TAKE A SELFIE?
HOW DID I EVEN GOT INVITED TO THIS THING?! I HAVE LIKE 500 FOLLOWERS! I FEEL SO LUCKY RIGHT NOW!!
500 FOLLOWERS? ...I MEAN, WE'RE ALL LUCKY TO BE HERE! HAVE FUN, 'K?
HAVE FUN, 'K?
WHAT? I'M JUST BEING NICE!
PFFHAHA! YOU'RE SO GOOD AT IT, TOO!

ALRIGHT, LADIES, WE'VE GOT YOU IN TWO SUPERIOR ROOMS ON OUR FOURTH FLOOR.
ENJOY YOUR STAY AT THE DESERT ROSE BY VALHALLA! AND THANKS... ...*TRAVAGANZA!*
HEY, WHO'S ROOMING WITH WHO?

DUH...

...ME AND CAROLINE.

...RIGHT??
HOW ABOUT THIS...
IS SHE GONNA F__KING SAY MEG?

...ME AND *MISTY!*
YAY!!

...WAIT, WHAT?

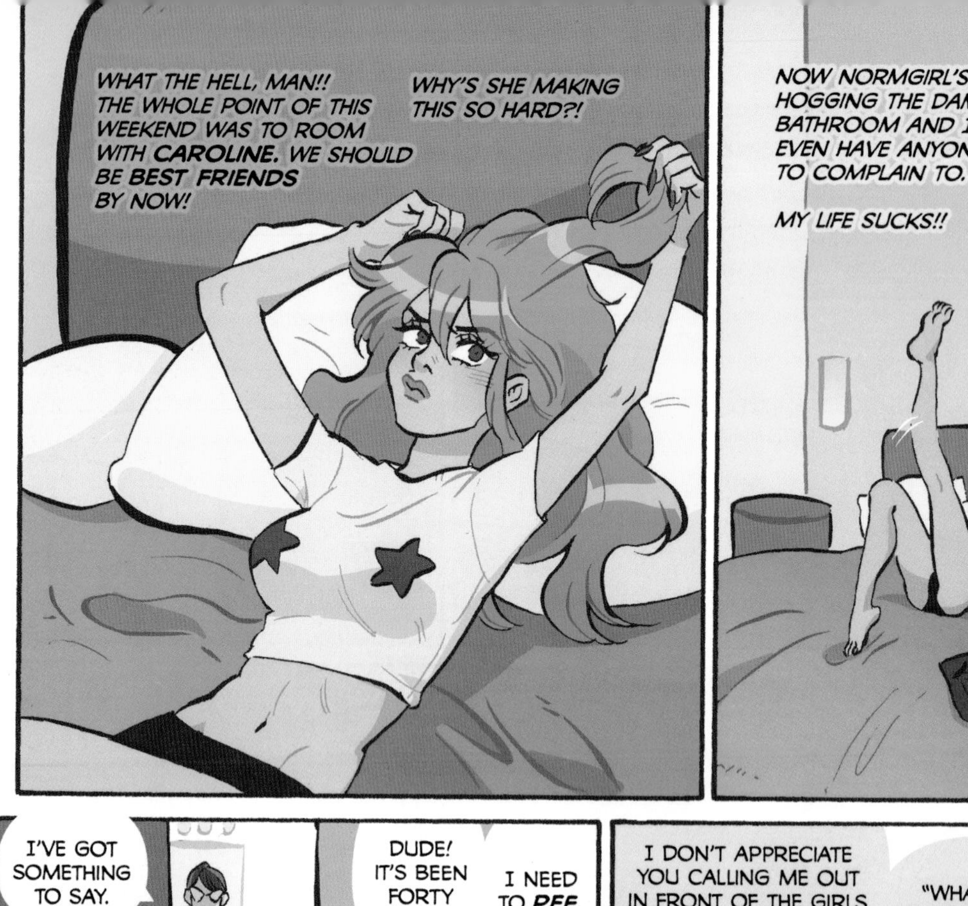
WHAT THE HELL, MAN!! THE WHOLE POINT OF THIS WEEKEND WAS TO ROOM WITH **CAROLINE.** WE SHOULD BE **BEST FRIENDS** BY NOW!
WHY'S SHE MAKING THIS SO HARD?!

NOW NORMGIRL'S HOGGING THE DAMN BATHROOM AND I DON'T EVEN HAVE ANYONE TO COMPLAIN TO.
MY LIFE SUCKS!!

I'VE GOT SOMETHING TO SAY.
DUDE! IT'S BEEN FORTY MINUTES!
I NEED TO ***PEE.***
I DON'T APPRECIATE YOU CALLING ME OUT IN FRONT OF THE GIRLS BACK THERE.
"WHAT DOES *SHE* KNOW ABOUT THE PERFECT WEDDING??"

I DIDN'T ***SAY*** THAT!!
YOU DIDN'T HAVE TO. I COULD SEE IT IN YOUR BIG BEAUTIFUL EYES! I'M INSECURE ENOUGH AS IT IS, YOU KNOW-- *I HAVE ANXIETY!!*
WHO DOESN'T?! WHAT DO YOU WANT, A *MEDAL?*

I WANT YOU TO TAKE YOUR TYPICAL *BAD* ATTITUDE AND SHOVE IT!

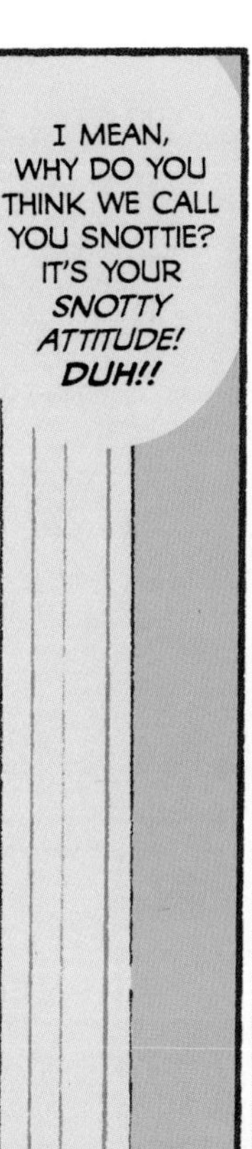
I MEAN, WHY DO YOU THINK WE CALL YOU SNOTTIE? IT'S YOUR *SNOTTY ATTITUDE!* ***DUH!!***

SLAM!
SPEECHLESS...

KNOK
KNOK

SLIP!
피부 재생
Face
Don't be mad.
*OK... WHY WOULD I BE MAD? LIKE I **AM**, BUT WHY WOULD SHE **THINK** THAT ABOUT ME?!*

413
WHAT'S *THAT?* A HIGH-END KOREAN FACE MASK?
SOMEONE SLIPPED IT UNDER YOUR DOOR, HUH? MUST HAVE BEEN A *GOOD FRIEND.*

Meanwhile.
I THINK I'M GONNA WALK AROUND THE HOTEL AND SHOOT SOME CANDIDS.
YOU OKAY TO HANG OUT IN THE ROOM BY YOURSELF, CHAR?
CHARLENE...?
twitch
I'M *FINE.*
WORKING ON YOUR SECRET PROJECT, HUH?
HEY... WHO'S THAT?
IS HE LIKE A SINGER OR SOMETHING?
I DON'T KNOW YET.
WHERE HAVE I SEEN HIM? WHO *IS* HE?
I DON'T *KNOW!*
SORRY, I'LL GET OUT OF YOUR HAIR.
DON'T STAY UP TOO LATE, OKAY?
smek

COULDN'T READ THE DIRECTIONS ON THIS KOREAN FACE MASK, BUT CUTEGIRL'S FACE IS LITERALLY A BABY'S ASS AND I'LL TRY ANYTHING ONCE.
JUST NEED TO TAKE MY...
...ALLERGY PILL???
I FORGOT MY PILLS?! NO WAY!!
I CAN'T HANDLE SNOTTIE LOTTIE RIGHT NOW!! THINGS ARE BAD ENOUGH!
CONGESTEX... ZERO GOOGLE RESULTS?! IT DOESN'T EXIST? I'M CAUGHT IN SOME FAKE DOCTOR'S WEB OF LIES!!
YOU HAVE REACHED THE OFFICES OF DR. YANG AND DR. RICK, ALLERGISTS!
OFFICE HOURS ARE MONDAY TO FRIDAY, NINE TO FIVE--
UGH, FINE, HE'S A REAL DOCTOR...
OKAY, CALM DOWN. IT'S A NEW EXPERIMENTAL TREATMENT, RIGHT?
IT MAKES SENSE THAT I WOULDN'T FIND RESULTS ONLINE...
BUT DR. DICK SAID IT WOULD BE BAD TO STOP SUDDENLY. HE SAID THERE WOULD BE SIDE EFFECTS... WHAT WERE THEY? THINK!
I COULD BE WAY OFF BASE, BUT I FEEL LIKE HE SAID SOMETHING ABOUT...

...HALLUCINATIONS?!?
KLIK
SHOVE
SLAM!

THIS ISN'T HAPPENING!!
DIVE

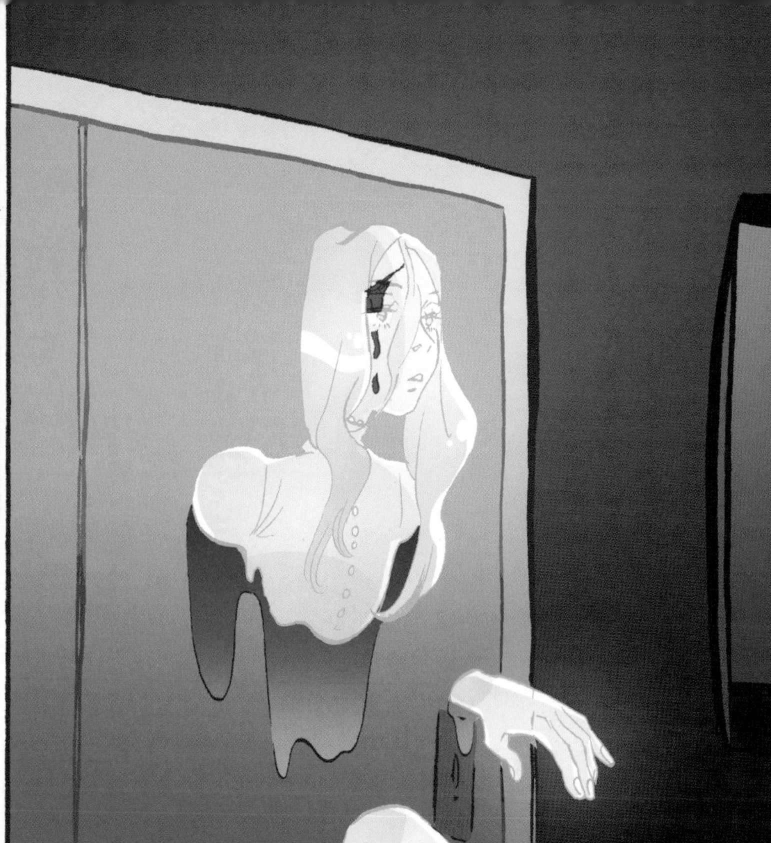

GOD!! WHERE THE HELL IS MEG WHEN YOU ACTUALLY NEED HER FOR ONCE?!

OKAY... CALM DOWN...
peek

...NO!! NO!!!! NO NO NO NO NO!!!

To: Haters (Group Text)
heyy someone pls come to my room asap. I just need a second opinion on something minor
hurry

WHO DARES ME TO TAKE MY TOP OFF?
DO IT, BETCH!
GUYS???

SHE'S ACTUALLY REALLY PRETTY... LIKE THE GHOST OF A HOT PERSON...
...WHAT KIND OF FACE MASK IS THAT...?
UMM...
IT'S, UHH, KOREAN?
MY WEIRD FRIEND ALWAYS GIFTS ME STUFF LIKE THIS.
...COOL... ...IS SHE A BRAND REP...?
WHAT? NO.
AT LEAST I DON'T THINK SO. MAYBE SHE IS...
OKAY, I'M TALKING ABOUT FACE MASKS WITH A GHOST! GET A GRIP, SNOTTIE!
...PLEASE TALK TO ME... I FEEL LIKE I'M FADING AWAY... ...I CAN'T EVEN REMEMBER MY NAME...
DAMN... WHAT DO YOU REMEMBER?
...I... REMEMBER... MY PHONE...
...I MISS MY PHONE THE MOST.

YOUR *PHONE?* I THOUGHT YOU WERE FROM OLDEN TIMES... NO OFFENSE!
...UGH, NO... I GOT THIS DRESS AT FREE PEOPLE AND NOW I'M STUCK WEARING IT FOR ETERNITY... AT LEAST IT WAS ON SALE...
...TELL ME... DID RIHANNA EVER RELEASE HER MAKEUP LINE...?
Y-YES?! YOU DIED ***SO RECENTLY...*** WHAT EVEN *HAPPENED* TO YOU?!

I DON'T KNOW... I GOT KILLED...! SOMEONE KILLED MY ASS...! WHO *CARES...?*
...I SAW THEM IN THE HOTEL TODAY... BUT WHAT AM *I* GONNA DO ABOUT IT...? ***NOTHING! ...I'M DEAD!***
...TELL ME... ...IS RIHANNA GOING TO BE HERE...? ...I WOULD DIE ALL OVER AGAIN...!
UM, EXCUSE ME? YOU WERE *MURDERED* AND YOUR KILLER IS ON THE LOOSE?!
...YES, BUT... RIHANNA...?
HAVE YOU *SEEN* THIS FESTIVAL? IT'S CORNY AS HELL! WHY WOULD RIHANNA SHOW UP?
CAN YOU PLEASE JUST ***TELL ME WHO KILLED YOU?!***

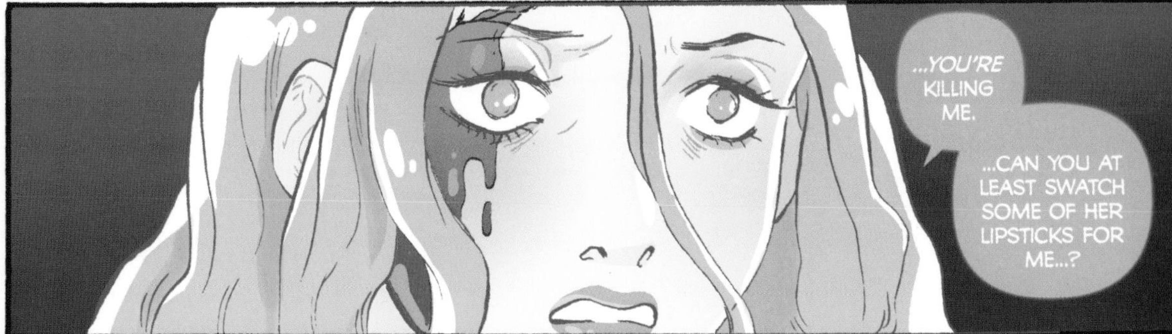
...YOU'RE KILLING ME.
...CAN YOU AT LEAST SWATCH SOME OF HER LIPSTICKS FOR ME...?

BAM!
OOP! HEY!
ARE YOU ALONE? THOUGHT I HEARD TALKING.

....

WHAT THE FUUAAH...!!!
?

WHERE WERE YOU?
THERE WAS A--
WHERE WERE YOU?
HOT TUB WITH THE GIRLS.
DON'T SAY A WORD!

WHAT? LIKE I CARE! HAVE LOADS OF FUN WITHOUT ME! WHATEVER!
I NEED TO MASSAGE THIS STUPID FACE MASK INTO MY STUPID FACE.
SEE, THIS BAD ATTITUDE IS EXACTLY WHY WE DIDN'T INVITE YOU TO THE HOT TUB!

SATURDAY
DR. DICK'S OFFICE IS CLOSED UNTIL MONDAY. IT'LL ALL BE OVER FOR ME BY THEN...
ESTHER PROBABLY STILL HAS A KEY TO MY PLACE... SHE COULD GRAB THE PILLS AND DRIVE OUT HERE... I BET SHE'D DO IT, TOO...
NO! I CAN'T KEEP ASKING ESTHER FOR HELP! SHE HAS A REAL JOB NOW... A REAL LIFE...
I DON'T DESERVE HER. I NEVER DID.
AVOCADO TOAST WITH EGG WAS A BAD IDEA. RUNNY... GREEN... IT'S LITERALLY ME...
SOON THEY'LL ALL KNOW WHAT A FRAUD I AM.
PART OF ME CAN'T WAIT...
WHY IS STUFF SO EASY FOR EVERYONE ELSE?
GUESS I'LL JUST FINISH MY TOAST AND HANG OUT WITH MY GHOST.
...BORED NOW... ...WHERE'S ALL THE MAKEUP AT...?

AS LONG AS I STAY INDOORS AND AVOID ALLERGENS...
...MAYBE I CAN FAKE MY WAY THROUGH THE REST OF THIS WEEKEND.
600
400
EEEEEEEEEEEEEE!!!
OR NOT!!
DAMN, GHOSTGIRL! CAN SHE CHILL??
EVERYTHING OKAY, HON?
EVERYTHING IS EXCELLENT!!
POSITIVITY-- I LIKE IT!
ME PRETENDING TO BE NORMAL FOR NORMGIRL... THE IRONY...
...SORRY... THOUGHT I SAW RIHANNA... BUT IT WAS ONLY A PAPER CUTOUT...
RIHANNA ISN'T COMING, OKAY?!
ISN'T SHE? THOUGHT I SAW HER...
OH, NEVER MIND. IT WAS JUST A PAPER CUTOUT.
SUNNY?! BAD JOKE!!

SO HOW'S IT... UH... HOW... ARE YOU?
UH, YOU KNOW. DOIN' FINE...
...DAMN... ...YOU AND HIM...?

WHAT'S WRONG?
NOT HERE.

P-PEOPLE CAN SEE US! WE'RE IN ***PUBLIC!***
...HEH... HE'S PRIME BEEF, GIRL... HIGH FIVE...

SUDDENLY.
EEEEEEEEE!!! YOU AND SUNNY *ARE* STILL TOGETHER! I KNEW IT! YOU GUYS ARE SUCH GOALS!
IT'S THAT GIRL FROM YESTERDAY!

MY FRIEND TOLD ME YOU BROKE UP, BUT I ALWAYS BELIEVED!
WE ARE *NOT* GOALS AND THIS IS A *REALLY* BAD TIME...
...SO COULD YOU PLEASE JUST STOP?? SMELLING ME???
WOW, YOUR HAIR SMELLS *AMAZING* UP CLOSE...

......

YOU WERE SO NICE TO ME YESTERDAY. I SHOULD HAVE *KNOWN* IT WAS AN ACT.
YOU NEVER EVEN ASKED MY NAME.
NO NO NO... HOW LONG HAVE THESE TWO BEEN WATCHING?
I-IT WASN'T AN ***ACT!*** I JUST GET *SO* OVERWHELMED AT THESE THINGS...
I'M HURT YOU WOULD THINK THAT! WHAT *IS* YOUR NAME?
WAIT...
THIS FAMILIAR FEELING...
IT'S HAPPENING! IT'S HAPPENING RIGHT NOW!
ALLERGY ATTACK IMMINENT!
OH MAN, I'M OVERWHELMED TOO! I'M SORRY I BLEW UP! MY NAME IS--
HEY-- HOLD THAT THOUGHT. I'LL BE RIGHT BACK!!!
SORRY SORRY SORRY SORRY!!
SO... RUDE...
ZOOM!
UH... SHE'S UNDER A LOT OF PRESSURE. SHE GETS *SO* OVER-WHELMED AT THESE THINGS--
YOU BOTH F■KING SUCK!!

I'M IN HELL. THIS IS A WEEKEND IN HELL.

LOTTIE? I SAW YOU WITH SUNNY... WHAT DID HE SAY?
KNOK

LISTEN... DON'T LET HIM GET TO YOU.
HE'S A GOOD GUY, BUT SOMEONE ELSE IS OUT THERE FOR YOU, I JUST KNOW IT!
UGHHH! SHUT UP!!

MEG... THIS ISN'T ABOUT SUNNY. I JUST NEED ME TIME, OKAY?
IT'S AN INFP THING!!
GET OUT OF HERE, MEG! I HATE YOU, MEG!!

I KNOW IT'S STUPID, BUT I SECRETLY HOPED WE'D BOTH GET MARRIED.
ME AND YOU AND SUNNY AND ASHLEY, ALL FRIENDS FOREVER.

...BUT NOTHING REALLY WORKS OUT THE WAY YOU IMAGINE, DOES IT?
GOD, MEG!!! LEAVE ME ALONE! LET ME DIE!

OH, GOD, LOTTIE, I REALLY MESSED UP!!!
MY WEDDING IS IN A SHAMBLES AND MY PRESENTATION IS NONEXISTENT! I'M A ***FRAUD***, LOTTIE! ***A FRAUD!!***

*DAMN, MEG, I THOUGHT WE WERE TALKING ABOUT **ME.***
SHE ALWAYS DOES THIS!

SHE'S A FUCKING MESS.

I DON'T TRUST ASHLEY ANYMORE! I LOVE HIM, BUT--
...GOD!!! IS THAT A HORRIBLE THING TO SAY?

I DIDN'T LET HIM MEET MY FRIENDS FOR TWO YEARS AND NOW HE JUST ACTS LIKE THAT'S NORMAL! AND I'M TOO *FAT* FOR HIM, I JUST KNOW IT. I JUST--

I JUST WANT SOMEONE TO HOLD ME TIGHT AND NEVER LET GO. IS THAT SO CRAZY?

SHOVE

O-OH MY GOD...

hug
...*THIS* IS WHY WE'VE BEEN CALLING YOU SNOTTIE?

THAT'S UNPLEASANT...

SO WE STAYED UP ALL NIGHT PUTTING MEG'S WEDDING PRESENTATION TOGETHER BASICALLY FROM SCRATCH.
JUST FRANTICALLY PULLING CONTENT OUT OF OUR ASSES AND SLAPPING IT INTO A POWERPOINT AT TOP SPEED.

THIS DUMB PRESENTATION WASN'T GOING TO CHANGE ANYONE'S LIFE, BUT IT WOULDN'T BE A COMPLETE WASTE OF FORTY MINUTES, EITHER.

VIRGIL?

...WHAT ARE YOU DOING HERE?

Lottie? It's Sunny. Are you safe? Is Meg with you?

yooooo

r u guys ok??

get out of bed!

10. WEEKEND, PART 2: WE'VE ONLY JUST BEGUN

...I WANT TO HELP... BUT... I JUST CAN'T SEEM TO REMEMBER...
...I'M SORRY.
LOOK, YOURE A GHOST, RIGHT? YOU FLOAT AROUND THIS HOTEL 24/7... YOU MUST SEE **EVERYTHING!** SO WAS THIS GIRL MURDERED OR WHAT?
...I DIDN'T SEE...
...BUT THE REASONS FOR ZOE'S DEATH...
...SEEM PRETTY CLEAR TO ME...
ZOE?!
YOU *KNEW* DEADGIRL? WHY DIDN'T YOU SAY ANYTHING?!

...WELL... IT'S MORE LIKE *SHE* KNEW *ME*... LIKE ALL THE DETAILS OF MY LIFE... SHE WAS PRACTICALLY STALKING ME...
...SHE WANTED TO ***BE*** ME.

ZOE WAS YOUR *CHARLENE!*

...WHATEVER THAT MEANS... JUST GLAD I'M FREE OF HER... ONLY PERK OF BEING DEAD... HAHA...
...MY THEORY IS SHE KNEW TOO MUCH... THAT'S WHY SHE GOT KILLED...

IN THAT CASE AREN'T YOU WORRIED *SHE'LL* COME BACK AS A GHOST?
...F*CK NO... DON'T SAY THAT... SHE TOTALLY WOULD!

BY MIDAFTERNOON, THANKSTRAVAGANZA LOOKED MORE LIKE THANKSPOCALYPSE, BUT NORMGIRL WOULDN'T LET US LEAVE...
YES, THE ROOMS WERE SPONSORED, BUT WE BARELY GENERATED ANY CONTENT! AND BESIDES, WE NEED TIME TO PROCESS THE TRAGEDY... WE LOST ONE OF OUR OWN TODAY.
UHH, SHE HAD LIKE FIVE HUNDRED FOLLOWERS, MEG... EVEN CAROLINE HAS MORE THAN THAT.
IT'S NOT ABOUT INDIVIDUAL ACHIEVEMENT, MISTY. IT'S ABOUT *COMMUNITY*. IT'S ABOUT GIVING BACK!
LIKE, I'M STILL BUMMED MY WEDDING PRESENTATION HAD TO BE CANCELED...
YEAH RIGHT, MEG, YOU DODGED A BULLET! AND THANKS FOR THE CREDIT...
HEYYY! WHY NOT SHARE IT WITH ***US,*** MEG?
YEAH, MEG, DON'T HOG ALL THE WEDDING PERFECTION TO YOURSELF.
OH, YOU'RE ***SO*** FUNNY! TOO BAD THIS IS NEITHER THE TIME NOR THE PLACE! A GIRL ***DIED***, REMEMBER?

WELL, THIS VIBE IS BUMMING ME OUT.
TRY TO CARRY ON WITHOUT ME, LADIES...
...I'M GONNA SEE IF I CAN SCARE UP A BARTENDER.
GOD... SHE'S SUCH AN INSPIRATION...

OKAY, SHE'S GONE!!!
THERE'S SOMETHING YOU NEED TO KNOW, LOTTIE!!

ON FRIDAY NIGHT... WE SAW THE DEAD GIRL!!
ONLY SHE *WASN'T DEAD YET*. REMEMBER WHEN WE ALL WENT TO THE HOT TUB WITHOUT INVITING YOU?

FRIDAY NIGHT
I DON'T MIND BEING TREATED LIKE A PIECE OF CRAP JUST 'CUZ I HAVE 527 FOLLOWERS!
IT LITERALLY DOESN'T EVEN *HIC* BOTHER ME! I'M JUST LUCKY TO BE HERE!!

BUT YOU! HOW DO YOU SLEEP? HOW CAN YOU EVEN **SHOW YOUR FACE?**
IT'S YOUR FAULT SHE'S GONE, YOU HAG!!

HAHAHA, WHO IS THIS CHICK?
I DON'T KNOW, BUT SHE MAD AT YOU...
TSK TSK...

SO WHAT'S YOUR POINT?!
THINK ABOUT IT! CAROLINE SWORE SHE DIDN'T KNOW THAT GIRL, BUT THE GIRL CLEARLY KNEW HER...
ISN'T THAT WEIRD?

UGH, GUYS, I'M SURE A LOT OF PEOPLE HAVE, LIKE, WEIRD UNREALISTIC CRUSHES ON HER OR WHATEVER.
BUT IF YOU'RE TRYING TO INSINUATE THAT CAROLINE HAD SOMETHING TO DO WITH THE GIRL'S DEATH... THAT IS SO STUPID.

THANKS FOR STICKING UP FOR ME, BABE. MAN, I CAN'T LEAVE YOU GOSSIPS ALONE FOR A SECOND, CAN I?
DIDN'T EVEN FIND A DAMN DRINK!
C-CAROLINE...! GOD, SHE'S BEEN IGNORING ME ALL WEEKEND... MAYBE THIS'LL PUT ME ON HER GOOD SIDE.

OKAY, I KNOW YOU GUYS SPENT WEEKS CURATING THE PERFECT OUTFITS FOR TONIGHT'S CLOSING GALA, AND YOU'RE ALL BUMMED YOU WON'T GET TO WALK SOME STUPID FAKE RED CARPET...
...SO I HAD AN IDEA. LET'S ALL DO A PHOTOSHOOT OUT IN THE DESERT AT MAGIC HOUR!
D-DESERT? HIGH WINDS... DUST... CACTI... AM I GONNA BE OKAY?

AHEM. WHAT IF ONE OF US HAS TERRIBLE ALLERGIES OR SOMETHMMF
WE'RE ALL FINE AND WE LOVE THE IDEA!!

GOD, CHAR, YOU HAD ME IN A PANIC! I WAS LOOKING EVERY-WHERE FOR YOU!
I THOUGHT IT WAS NEW YEAR'S EVE ALL OVER AGAIN!
SUNNY... I WAS IN THE BATHROOM.
DON'T ***TRIVIALIZE*** THIS! MY FEELINGS ARE VALID, OKAY?!

IT WASN'T *ABOUT* YOUR FEELINGS... I JUST HAD TO POO!
C'MON...
...IT'S NOT *SAFE* HERE. PACK YOUR THINGS! NO, ***I'LL*** DO IT...
SUNNYYY! DON'T MESS UP MY STUFF!

BUT WHAT ABOUT THE TIMES WHEN YOU MESS UP YOUR *OWN* STUFF, CHARLENE? WHAT SHOULD I DO ***THEN?!***
JESUS, SUNNY! IF YOU WANT TO LEAVE, LET ME PACK! QUIT *BABYING* ME! GO TAKE A WALK OR SOMETHING!
CH-CHAR... I'M *SORRY!*
YOU'RE A GOOD EGG! YOU REALLY ARE!!

HANKSTRAVAG
SNAP!
HEH, NOT BAD! GETTIN' SOME GOLD HERE, SUNNY-BOY...

HOTEL SECURITY, HUH?
THIS GUY IS HAVING A ROUGH DAY.

WAIT A SECOND.
IS THAT...?

H-HOTEL SECURITY MY FOOT!

STAFF ONLY
STAFF ONLY
STAFF ONLY
...DESERVE A LIFE FREE OF MURDER AND MAYHEM. THAT'S *MY* LINE OF WORK! HAHAHA.
HAHA... YEAH...
LOTTIE...?!

THIS IS WHAT I GET FOR SNEAKING AWAY FOR SOME INFP TIME! DOESN'T THIS GUY HAVE CRIMES TO SOLVE? HE'S LIKE **OBSESSED** WITH ME!
SO YEAH, IN GENERAL, PLEASE FEEL FREE TO CALL OR TEXT IF YOU HAVE ANY QUESTIONS OR CONCERNS, LOTTIE.

SNAP!
SUNNY?!
WHY IS **HE** STILL HERE? WHY ARE EITHER OF THEM STILL HERE?!

SUNNY DAY!! DELETE THAT RIGHT NOW!
SEND ME A COPY! SEND ME THAT.

YOU TWO LOOK COZY. OUTSIDE THE LAPD'S USUAL JURISDICTION, HUH JOHN?
I'M HERE AS PART OF A SPECIAL INVESTIGATION, BUD. TAKE ANOTHER PIC FOR MY MOM, OKAY?

LOTTIE WON'T MIND--

......

UGHH! CAN YOU BELIEVE THOSE TWO?
...THOSE TWO GORGEOUS MEN FIGHTING OVER YOU...? YOUR LIFE IS AMAZING...
FIGHTING OVER ME? MORE LIKE SHOWING THEIR ASSES!
...YOU'RE CRAZY... THEY'RE SO HOT...
HOT?? THIS IS HOW YOU GOT KILLED, ISN'T IT?
SUNNY'S MY EX. ALL HE DOES NOW IS WORK OUT! HE LOOKS REAL BIG... NOT LIKE I CARE! AND JOHN... HE'S TOO SHORT. PLUS HE'S A COP.
OOH... INTO IT...
...ALTHOUGH RIGHT NOW I'M INTO ANYTHING WITH A HEARTBEAT AND A D*CK...
GODDDD! YOU'RE THE WORST...
BEEP!
UHHHH... DID I GO IN THE WRONG ROOM?
IT'S ME! YOUR NEW ROOMIE!

ALL THIS TROUBLE FOR ONE NIGHT? YOU'RE *OBSESSED* WITH ME.
I *MISS* YOU! PLUS CAROLINE ***SUCKS.***

I'M SURE! YOU'VE BEEN TWO PEAS IN A POD ALL WEEKEND.
GOD, LOTTIE, CAN'T YOU TELL WHEN I'M *FAKING NICE?* I'VE BEEN INVESTIGATING HER ON YOUR BEHALF! LOOK AT THIS...

WHAT'S IT GONNA BE, PICS OF HER TOOTH-BRUSH?
YOU'LL SEEEEE!

FASHIONISTA MISSING, LAST SEEN AT CA MOTEL
WHAT'S THIS?
THIS IS NOTHING. HANG ON.
...WAIT...
*IS THAT **GHOSTGIRL?** HOLY SH*T, SHE'S REAL?!*

GO BACK!!! I WAS READING THAT!!
BUT CAROLINE'S TOOTHBRUSH! ISN'T IT GROSS??

MEANWHILE.

PSSSST! GHOSTGIRL!
...IS THAT WHAT YOU'RE CALLING ME? THAT'S MESSED UP...
WOULD YOU RATHER I CALL YOU...
...YOLANDA SINCLAIR?!
...EW... WAS THAT MY NAME...? NOT FEELING IT...
I READ AN ARTICLE ABOUT YOU. IT SAID YOU WERE A FASHION BLOGGER JUST LIKE ME...
ONE DAY YOU DISAPPEARED AND PEOPLE BARELY NOTICED, 'CUZ YOU SPENT SO MUCH TIME TRAVELING.
IT SAID BY THE TIME YOU WERE DECLARED MISSING, THE MOTEL WHERE YOU LAST STAYED HAD BEEN FULLY RENOVATED...
NOW YOU HAUNT THE HALLS OF THE FIVE-STAR HOTEL WHERE YOUR BONES ARE BURIED, AND YOUR MURDERER STILL ROAMS FREE!!

...WOW... SOUNDS LIKE A MOVIE OR SOMETHING... GET MY AGENT ON THE PHONE... LOL...
EXCUSE ME, CAN WE TAKE THIS SERIOUSLY FOR A SECOND?! I DON'T WANT TO END UP LIKE YOU! NO OFFENSE!

...SO WHY DON'T YOU GO HOME? ...ZOE'S DEAD... RIHANNA NEVER EVEN SHOWED...
...WHY WOULD THE KILLER STAY? ...WHY ARE YOU HERE?

...YOU KNOW, I WAS ALMOST A FASHION DESIGNER... BUT THAT WAS ANOTHER LIFE.
UM, WOW... CAN I GO?
OH YEAH, YOU'RE FREE TO GO! DON'T FORGET TO HIT ME UP ON INSTAGRAM!
DAMN IT, JOHN! YOU CAN'T USE POLICE BUSINESS TO PICK UP GIRLS!

ABE! H-HEY! SOMETIMES IT'S THE ONLY WAY THEY'LL TALK TO ME, Y'KNOW?
JOHN... LOOK. I'M MISSING MY KID'S QUIDDITCH MATCH FOR THIS, SO I'LL MAKE IT QUICK.

YOU'RE IN BIG FUCKIN' TROUBLE, PARTNER! THE CHIEF WANTS YOUR ASS AND I'M HERE TO *DRAG IT BACK*...

...UNLESS YOU CAN GIVE ME SOME ***CONCRETE PROOF*** ON THIS CASE *RIGHT NOW.*
SURE! N-NO PROBLEM!

I SWEAR I'LL FIND SOME!!!

WHEN WE GOT DOWNSTAIRS, CAROLINE HAD ORDERED **HIGH TEA** FOR THE GROUP. KIND OF INAPPROPRIATE WITH WHAT'S BEEN GOING ON, BUT WHATEVER I GUESS...
TO US!
HATERS' BRUNCH FOREVER!

OOH, DELICIOUS!
HUH. UNUSUAL FLAVOR...

...IS THIS TEA SINGLE ORIGIN?

AND THEN WE HEADED INTO THE DESERT.

THE LIGHT IS PERFECT! WHO AM I SHOOTING?

HOW ABOUT--
HOW ABOUT ME AND CAROLINE?? YOU KNOW? JUST TO TRY!!

LOOK AT US!! IF THERE'S ONE THING I'VE LEARNED THIS WEEKEND, IT'S THAT THE ONLY WAY TO GET WHAT I WANT IS TO ***SEIZE THE DAMN MOMENT!***

HAVING FUN? I KNOW IT'S NO *VOGUE* SHOOT...
YEAH, IT'S CHILL. NICE *JACKET,* BY THE WAY.

YOU NOTICED... IT'S *YOURS!* I HAD IT DRY-CLEANED AFTER OUR FIRST DATE...

FIRST DATE?

I MEAN--
SO TO SPEAK--
THAT ONE TIME--

MAN, SNOTTIE.
YOU REALLY WISH I WAS YOUR GIRLFRIEND, HUH?

SHE DID NOT JUST--!!

LOTTIE! YOU PROBABLY CAN'T HEAR ME OVER THE WIND, BUT I LIKE WHERE YOU'RE GOING WITH THIS! VERY RAW!!
WHAT??

CAROLINE!! IS SHE FOR REAL RIGHT NOW?
HOW ABOUT A NEW POSE?

ME NEXT!! ME AND SNOTTIE! CAN YOU HEAR ME??
STOP CALLING HER THAT! IT'S INCREDIBLY UNKIND!
ARE YOU YELLING AT ME OR ARE WE JUST YELLING?

WHAT THE F*CK IS HAPPENING...?

ME AM SNOTTIE!
NYAHH!

ARE THEY OKAY?
SHH.
DON'T WORRY ABOUT THEM. JUST BE.
I'M DOING MY BEST...

WOW... WHEN WAS THE LAST TIME I SAW THE STARS?
IT'S SO WEIRD TO BE OUT OF THE CITY...
I FEEL SO SMALL, SO INSIGNIFICANT.
EVERYTHING I DO IS STUPID.
MY WHOLE STUPID LIFE...
GOD...
WHAT TIME IS IT?
WHERE'S MISTY AND MEG?
THEY'RE FINE. RELAX.
WHAT WAS THAT YOU WERE SAYING ABOUT THE STARS?
THE STARS? WAS THAT OUT LOUD?
JUST... UH... WHEN DID I LAST SEE A SKY LIKE THIS? I THINK IT WAS IN A DREAM... A DREAM ABOUT YOU.
YOU HAD A DREAM ABOUT ME?
SEVERAL...

YOU'RE SHAKING--
WAIT, ARE YOU *LAUGHING* AT ME?!
AHAHAHAHA! SORRY, I JUST-- ***MULTIPLE DREAMS?*** HOW *MANY*?? YOU'RE SO WEIRD!!
GOD, CAROLINE, WHAT THE ***FUCK!*** I CAN'T KEEP UP WITH YOU ANYMORE!!
I'M TRYING TO BE YOUR ***FRIEND!*** DON'T YOU SEE I'M *SUFFERING?* WHAT DO YOU ***WANT*** FROM ME?!

.....
WELL THAT SHUT YOU UP.
AHAHA, SORRY, JUST... I'M HIGH... WE'RE ALL HIGH... BECAUSE I PUT MUSHROOMS IN THE TEA! AHAHAHA!
YOU PUT WHAT IN THE TEA?!
DON'T FREAK OUT! IT GETS WORSE IF YOU FREAK OUT. C'MON, LET'S FIND THE GIRLS.
C'MON!
WHY IS THIS HAPPENING TO ME?!
HELL... HELL! I'M IN HELL!!

FINALLY... THE HOTEL...

Desert ROSE
MOTOR INN
NO VACANCY
WAIT... IS THIS RIGHT?

1

THIS CAN'T BE REAL!!
IT'S NOT!!
IT'S NOT!!!
LOTTIE!

ESTHER DUMONT
MY EX-INTERN
STYLE: perfect
I MISS HER: so much
esert ro
by valha
HEY!
PSILO-SOMETHING MUSHROOMS... YOU KNOW, THE KIND THAT MAKE YOU TRIP BALLS?
SOMEONE SLIPPED A PINCH OF THEM IN YOUR TEA.
PRECIOUS WATER
YOU GUYS MUST HAVE HAD A WILD NIGHT!
...ESTHER... HOW HAVE I BEEN LIVING WITHOUT YOU?!

by valhalla
THIS HOTEL IS A *MESS*. YOUR TEA FROM LAST NIGHT IS STILL SITTING OUT ON THE TABLE... IT'S LIKE A *GHOST TOWN* IN THERE. WHAT HAPPENED?
I ALMOST *BECAME* A GHOST. I ALMOST *DIED*. YOU SAVED MY LIFE, ESTHER DUMONT!! YOU'RE A REAL LIFE ANGEL! BUT HOW'D YOU ***KNOW***?

CHECK YOUR TEXTS LATER. YOU SENT ME LIKE A *MILLION*. PICS, VIDEO, THE WORKS.
GLUG

Y'KNOW, IT'S *MONDAY*... YOU'RE LUCKY I HAD THE DAY OFF! BUT THEN, MAYBE IT'S LIKE MY MOM SAYS: EVERYTHING HAPPENS FOR A REASON.
C'MON, LET'S GET YOU CLEANED UP.

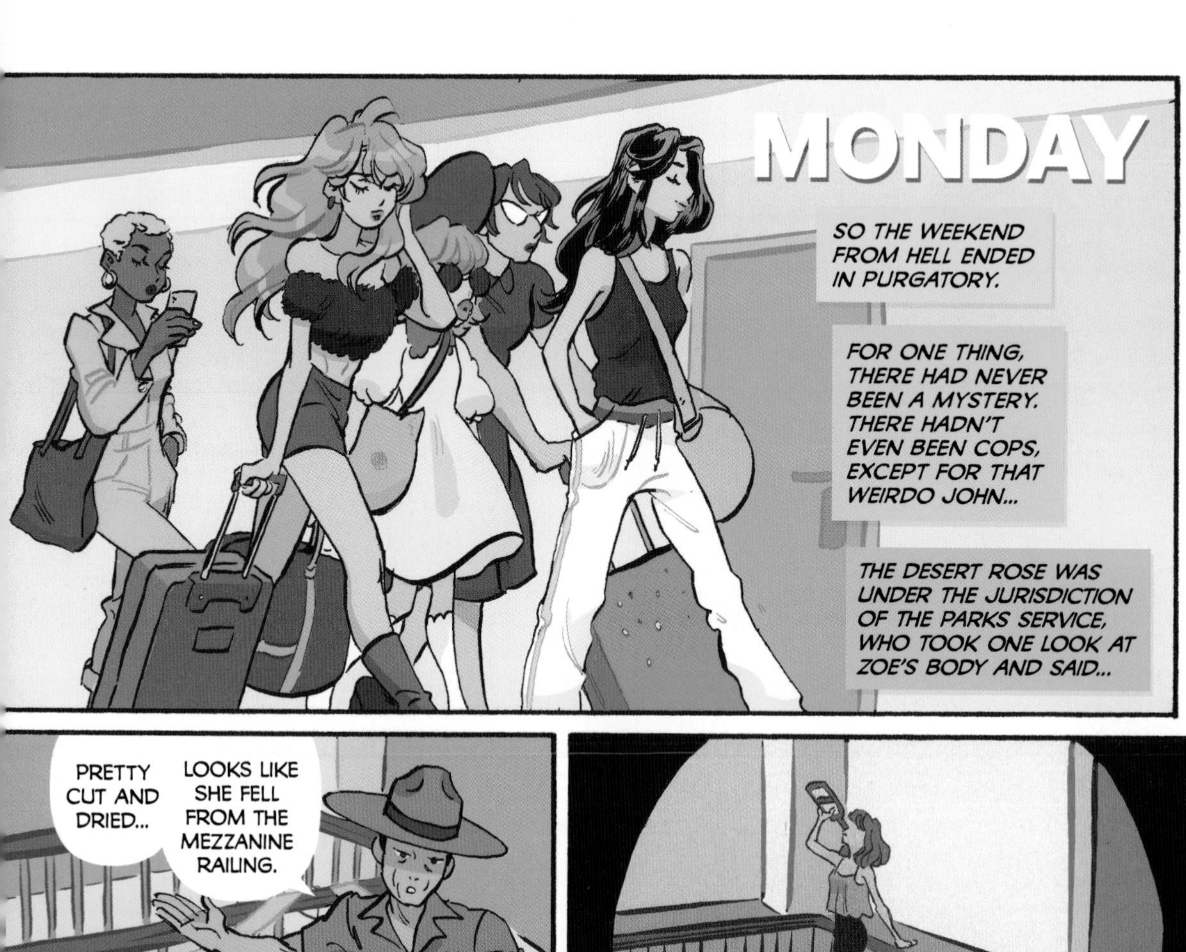
MONDAY
SO THE WEEKEND FROM HELL ENDED IN PURGATORY.
FOR ONE THING, THERE HAD NEVER BEEN A MYSTERY. THERE HADN'T EVEN BEEN COPS, EXCEPT FOR THAT WEIRDO JOHN...
THE DESERT ROSE WAS UNDER THE JURISDICTION OF THE PARKS SERVICE, WHO TOOK ONE LOOK AT ZOE'S BODY AND SAID...

PRETTY CUT AND DRIED...
LOOKS LIKE SHE FELL FROM THE MEZZANINE RAILING.

IT ONLY TOOK THEM A FEW HOURS TO COMB THROUGH THE SECURITY FOOTAGE... AND THERE WAS ZOE, DRUNK AS F*CK.

I FEEL EMPTIED OUT.

fenty swatches for a friend

SO IF ZOE JUST DIED FOR NO REASON, WHAT WAS THE **POINT** OF ALL THIS?

SUNNY?
HEY...
W-WHAT'S UP? I'M JUST... I'M NOT DOING ANYTHING.

...I'M GAY.

DID ANY OF IT **MEAN** ANYTHING? IS THERE A LESSON TO BE LEARNED?

MAYBE I'M JUST TOO CLOSE TO THE WHOLE THING.

OR TOO STUPID.

BUT AFTER EVERYTHING THAT HAPPENED, THERE'S ONLY ONE THING I KNOW FOR SURE.
ding!
From: Caroline
we kissed lol
shit is this the group text
jk it's not
hang soon?
CAROLINE...
RISE AND SHINE! I BROUGHT VEGAN DONUTS!

...ESTHER? GOOD MORNING...
HEYYY... REMEMBER HOW I SAVED YOUR DAMN LIFE AND YOU OWE ME BIG?

...I HAD AN IDEA. A *BUSINESS* IDEA. AND I THINK YOU'RE GONNA LIKE IT.
.....
TO BE CONTINUED

LOTTIE LOTTIE LOTT

COVER GALLERY
ISSUE 10

IDENTICAL TWINS
Cutegirl
a.k.a.
Misty
Real name:
Winnie. C.

Leslie's Comment

by Leslie Hung

BONNIE

Misty's twin sister Bonnie is a bit of an aspirational figure. I think her style and design resonated a lot with my same-age friends. We all want to have that simple, effortless style — slightly relaxed, but still form-fitting and classic. Going with a natural, contemporary hairstyle felt like a young hip mom thing to do. If she existed in real life, everywhere she went, people would look, and they would approve.

VIRGIL

Virgil was the new character I spent the most time thinking through in terms of style, because I wanted him to be purposely confounding. Characters with glasses tend to have a more subdued look, but I wanted him to have many "secrets" within the way he dresses and presents himself. He's the character that has the most piercings, after Cutegirl (she has 12-13.) Virgil is a very hedonistic dresser, with easily the most expensive wardrobe, although you would never be able to tell unless you kept up with the trends. He's very slim, and can, and WILL, wear anything. This outfit and color scheme was heavily influenced by **Vetements**, like thousand dollar **Champion** hoodies and huge metal hoops that became super popular late 2016. Everyone rips them off now, so it's not as cool, which means Virgil probably tossed this hoodie.

PINKEYE

Early on I painted Misty with an eye patch and knew it would have to return. Cutegirl is a bit like a small animal that makes itself more intimidating and scary by puffing its fur out, so this gothic lolita inspired outfit is a bit of all of that. It's playing into the sweet lolita realm, with the gigantic bonnet and the tiered cream cake feel of the entire look. It's a stark contrast to Snottie's outfit in this scene, which is body conscious but subdued.

REUNITED

Snottie's outfit here is simple but sexy. The booties are blue suede. Caroline's outfit is a play on the one she was wearing way back on their first date, but I wanted it to look dingier and slightly gross, like she hadn't showered in weeks (too busy playing video games and being a shut-in). Caroline is a character who swings between extreme moods very easily. Her capriciousness makes me uneasy.

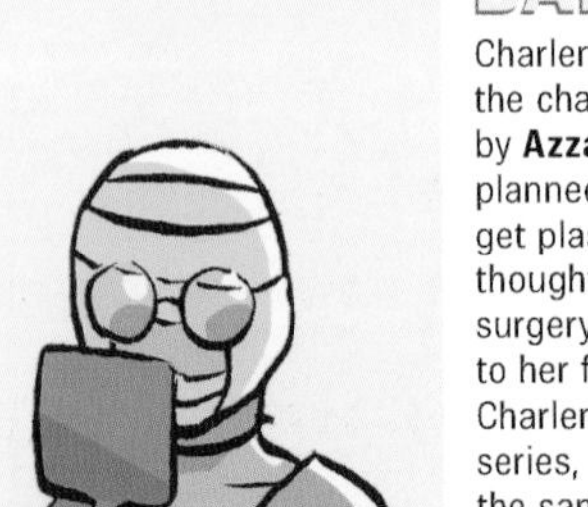

BANDAGES

Charlene's face bandages were inspired by the character of Milo Garret from **100 Bullets** by **Azzarello** and **Risso**. Bryan initially planned for Charlene to achieve her dreams, get plastic surgery and look amazing, but I thought it would be funnier if her plastic surgery was successful in that it restored her to her former self. I really enjoy drawing Charlene and her antics throughout the series, although I don't know if people get the same level of enjoyment from reading and seeing them.

FLOWER BOOBS

Brands by influencers or that start on Instagram tend to be more trendy and therefore have less longevity and timelessness, but also capture a moment in time that's hard to express with more classic pieces. I wanted to explore more accessory-less outfits for Snottie, but also played a lot with some cheeky motifs centered around her chest in this arc. Snottie doesn't have enough confidence in her personality and inner life, so she focuses on accentuating all her "good" traits outward.

SNOTPUPPY

This is one of those visual gags that people either understood completely or didn't get at all. I've had a lot of random conversations about what kind of animals the characters in Snotgirl would be. Even before the first issue, my friend **Em Partridge** drew Snottie as a green cocker spaniel. Later on, when the idea of inserting more strange dreams (based off of my own strange dreams?) came up as a narrative element, we loved the idea of Snottie as a beautiful baby puppy.

BLUE DRESS

A bit Ann Takamaki (**Persona 5**), a bit **Jojo's Bizarre Adventure**, but all Snottie, in its nonsensical blue vinyl glory. I struggled with this outfit and kept adding/removing elements while penciling; this one panel was where it all came together, so I had to go through after and update the rest.

THE BOYS

Ashley is very shiny and pink, and I just wanted his entire look to be very preppy with tons of light pastels. It's very important to me to have very distinct style differences between the boys, even if it's only obvious to me. Men's fashion in general is a bit more of a mystery to me, so I tend to lean more towards my own personal tastes when dressing the boys, over what I think a lot of men would typically gravitate towards. Ashley's style veers more towards dandyism and is a bit flashy and tacky, as opposed to John's suits, which are understated and professional. Sunny is more of a true gym rat, so his look, including the headband, are a bit more on the practical side (except for his hair!).

BUSH

Cutegirl's bush outfit is a play off of an illustration by **René Gruau** of a woman dressed as a flower bouquet (incidentally, **Jeremy Scott** designed a dress based on this same illustration for **Moschino** Spring 2018.) The flower headpiece was a trend in Chinese street fashion a few years ago, I always thought it was hilarious and kind of whimsical, like **Pikmin** or something, and the gag later on when Misty needs to use the bathroom and is uncomfortable and sweaty made for a lot of expressiveness in the flower.

UNIFORMS

Virgil is often in disguise and sneaking around, but he always likes to insert a bit of his personal style. Note that we've already seen Virgil in tiny shorts twice. Not suspicious at all! Totally blending in!

SHORT FILM

There are two Misties in Tokyo Twinsies: Cute Innocent Misty and Cool Lottie Misty. Cutegirl is anything but subtle; her constant assertions that she and Lottie are best friends and twins even manifest in her "short" film. In the film, her creampuff outfit and big red bows are meant to symbolize lost naiveté, while her leather jacket and beret with a sequined skirt show off a tough, adventurous, yet girly vibe. (Misty is perfectly capable of dressing more chic and cool; she *chooses* not to.) For the presentation look, I opted for the repeating wing theme; very late '90s **CLAMP**. Cutegirl owns about 50 different berets with different motifs, and she brought her own microphone, based on the ones K-pop idols use on variety shows.

GHOSTGIRL

I used to shop at **Free People** a lot when I was a teen, mostly just buying things that were on sale, but I hadn't really thought about the brand in years. Trends come and go, and apparently the trends that were a thing when I was in high school are now back in style. I liked the idea of the ghost stuck in a dress that could easily be either interpreted as very boho chic or a bit modern Victorian. The ambiguity of whether something is old or new, or if it looks good or bad, is something that I think even super-fashionable people struggle with at times.

POOF

In the last two chapters, Snottie has to dress to impress not just everyone at Thankstravaganza, but Caroline, too. It's kind of a tall order, but I felt that a feathery furry mess on Snottie was actually somehow a good look that softened her a bit. Totally a casual brunch outfit.

RED PANTS

Lottie's outfits have gotten a bit more loud and trendy as the series goes on. I initially wanted her style to be primarily based on body-hugging silhouettes with trendy color combinations, but there's something evocative to me about Lottie wearing clothes that won't last a season in her closet. The ephemeral nature of how fashionable/current any given outfit can be is something that thrills me. It's part of the essence of the whole series: how app interfaces, phone faces, and heel shapes change over time based on the trends. Also, i just thought she looked really good in this outfit, kind of like Christmas.

THANKSTRAVAGANZA!

Here I'm continuing to put Snottie in trendy pieces that won't make it a year in her closet — maybe a couple of months. The whole outfit is a bit moody in tone, which tends to happen when she ends up interacting one-on-one with Sunny.

MEG

Meg gets overlooked among the girls, but then that's kind of her role in the series. She's a bit of a matronly character despite being the median age between Snottie and Misty, but chapter 9 shows more of her personality. She's self-conscious about a lot of things, which manifests in the way she dresses herself. I originally had her in a leather motorcycle jacket as well, but it seemed too hot or cumbersome on a convention floor. I wanted Meg to have a nice outfit for when she actually lets herself be vulnerable in front of Lottie. It's a scene I've been wanting to show for a while. I think that a lot of Snottie's closest relationships are often misconstrued and misunderstood. Maybe they're not good at being friends, but they *are* friends.

ESTHER

She's back!! Esther is wearing an outfit that I own (in different colors): a **Big Bud Press** jumpsuit with a simple pair of mules. This is a good outfit for a career woman like Esther. It's fun and cute, but still functional.

Leslie Hung
Feb-March 2018

MAGIC HOUR SHOOT

Snottie's daring dress shows a lot of skin, but it's such a fun contrast to Caroline's bomber from the first issue. Her body-chain is a bit of a callback to how she was styled in the beginning of the series. Caroline's look is sexy and dramatic, yet casual. It's a very simple/classic shape on her. I think she likes dresses that fit easily (no need for fashion tape.) I asked Rachael to make it sparkly and sequined and she did a really nice job. Of course Caroline is wearing **Chucks** with her dress.